The Supporters' Guide to Scottish Football 1997

EDITOR
John Robinson

Fifth Edition

CONTENTS

British Library Cataloguing in Publication Data
A catalogue record for this book is available from the British Library
ISBN 0-947808-71-X

Printed by Adlard Print & Typesetting Services, The Old School, The Green, Ruddington, Notts. NG11 6HH

FOREWORD

We wish to thank the club secretaries of the Scottish League, Highland League, East of Scotland League and South of Scotland League for their assistance in providing the information contained in this guide. We also wish to thank Michael Robinson (page layouts), Ceri Sampson (cover artwork), Chris Ambler (photos), J.H. Grant (Highland League) and David McDonald (East of Scotland League), for their invaluable assistance.

This year we have revisited many of the grounds detailed and have provided new ground photos where possible.

When using this guide, readers should note that most clubs also extend the child concessionary prices to include Senior Citizens.

As part of our ongoing aim to improve our publications, readers are invited to let us know if they experience any difficulties with this guide, particularly incorrect directions, phone numbers or club information.

Finally, we would like to wish our readers a happy and safe spectating season.

John Robinson
EDITOR

WELSH NATIONAL STADIUM

Re-Opened for Football: 31st May 1989
Location: Cardiff City Centre, CARDIFF
Telephone: (01222) 390111 (Ground)
Telephone: (01222) 372325 (F.A. of Wales)
Address: The National Ground, Cardiff Arms Park, Westgate Street, CARDIFF, Wales

Pitch Size: 110 × 69yds
Ground Capacity: 51,374
Seating Capacity: 42,355
(40,240 for Football Matches)
Note: This stadium will be closed late in 1996 for redevelopment. At the time of publication the alternate venues are not known

GENERAL INFORMATION
Car Parking: City Centre Car Parks
Coach Parking: By Police Direction
Nearest Railway Station: 5-10 minutes walk
Nearest Bus Station: 5 minutes walk
Nearest Police Station: Cardiff Centre
Police Force: South Wales
Police Telephone No.: (01222) 222111

GROUND INFORMATION
Family Facilities: **Location of Stand**:
Lower Tier of North & South Stands
Capacity of Stand: Not Specified

DISABLED SUPPORTERS INFORMATION
Wheelchairs: Accommodated in Disabled Section -
North Side of West Stand - spaces for 24 wheelchairs
Disabled Toilets: Yes

ADMISSION INFO (1996/97 PRICES)
Adult Seating: £6.00 - £20.00
Child Seating: Half-price in Family Enclosures
Programme Price: £2.00
FAX Number: (01222) 343961
Note: Prices vary depending on the opponents & type of game.

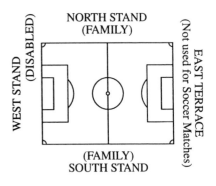

Travelling Supporters Information:
Routes: Exit M4 at Junction 29 and take A48(M) following signs for Cardiff City Centre (via A470). Use City Centre Public Car Parks.
From Cardiff Central Railway Station: Proceed past Bus Station, cross Wood Street and turn down Westgate Street (alongside the back of the Royal Hotel).

WEMBLEY STADIUM

Opened: 1923	**Ground Capacity**: 80,000
Location: Wembley, Middlesex HA9 0DW	**Seating Capacity**: 80,000
Telephone: Box Office (0181) 900-1234	**Record Attendance**: 100,000
Telephone: Administration (0181) 902-8833	**Pitch Size**: 115 × 75yds
FAX Number: (0181) 903-4818	

GENERAL INFORMATION
Guided Tours Available: Telephone (0181) 902-8833 (ext. 3346) for details
Parking: Car Park for over 7,000 vehicles
Nearest Railway Stations: Wembley Park, Wembley Central, Wembley Complex (5-10 minutes walk)
Nearest Police Station: Mobile Unit in front of the Twin Towers
Police Force Responsible for Crowd Control: Metropolitan
Police Telephone No.: (0181) 903-4818

GROUND INFORMATION
All Sections of the Ground are Covered
Family Facilities: Location of Stand:
Family Enclosure, North Stand

DISABLED SUPPORTERS INFORMATION
Wheelchairs: Limited Facilities Available
Disabled Toilets: Yes
The Blind: No Special Facilities

ADMISSION INFO (1996/97 PRICES)
Admission £12.00 - £30.00; depending on the game and ground position. Also a £1 per seat booking fee
(Accompanied Children - half price in family enclosure)

OLYMPIC WAY & TWIN TOWERS
(ROYAL BOX SIDE)
NORTH STAND   FAMILIES
(STADIUM OFFICE END) WEST TERRACE
(PLAYERS TUNNEL END) EAST TERRACE
SOUTH STAND

How to get to Wembley By Road

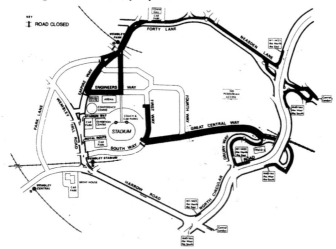

5

HAMPDEN STADIUM

Opened: 1903
Location: In the 'Mount Florida' area of Glasgow, South East of the River Clyde
Telephone: Administration (0141) 632-1275
FAX Number: (0141) 636-1612
Address: Hampden Park, Mount Florida, Glasgow G42 9BA

Ground Capacity: 34,000
Seating Capacity: 34,000
Record Attendance: 150,239 (Scotland vs. England 17th April 1937)
Pitch Size: 115 × 75yds
When development complete - capacity 60,000

GENERAL INFORMATION
Car Parking: Car Park for 1,200 vehicles
Coach Parking: Stadium Car Park
Nearest Railway Station: Mount Florida & Kings Park (both 5 minutes walk)
Nearest Police Station: Aikenhead Road, Glasgow G42
Police Force Responsible for Crowd Control: Strathclyde
Police Telephone No.: (0141) 422-1113

GROUND INFORMATION
Family Facilities: **Location of Stand**:
Varies from game to game
Capacity of Stand: -

DISABLED SUPPORTERS INFORMATION
Wheelchairs: Accommodated in temporary disabled spectators section in front of the North Stand
Disabled Toilets: None during redevelopment
The Blind: Personal Commentaries

NORTH STAND

WEST STAND

EAST STAND

SOUTH STAND
(UNDER REDEVELOPMENT)

MOUNT FLORIDA   KINGS PARK

Travelling Supporters Information:
Routes: From the South: Take the A724 to the Cambuslang Road and at Eastfield branch left into Main Street and follow through Burnhill Street and Westmuir Place into Prospecthill Road. Turn left into Aikenhead Road and right into Mount Annan for Kinghorn Drive and the Stadium; From the South: Take the A77 Fenwick Road, through Kilmarnock Road into Pollokshaws Road then turn right into Langside Avenue. Pass through Battle Place to Battlefield Road and turn left into Cathcart Road. Turn right into Letherby Drive, right into Carmunnock Road and 1st left into Mount Annan Drive for the Stadium; From the North & East: Exit M8 Junction 15 and passing Infirmary on left proceed into High Street and cross the Albert Bridge into Crown Street. Join Cathcart Road and proceed South until it becomes Carmunnock Road. Turn left into Mount Annan Drive and left again into Kinghorn Drive for the Stadium.

SCOTTISH FOOTBALL LEAGUE

Founded
1890

Secretary
Mr. Peter Donald

Address
188 West Regent Street
GLASGOW   G2 4RY

Phone
(0141) 248-3844

ABERDEEN FC

Founded: 1903
Admitted to League: 1904
Former Name(s): None
Nickname: 'The Dons'
Ground: Pittodrie Stadium, Pittodrie Street, Aberdeen   AB2 1QH
Record Attendance: 45,061 (13/3/54)

Colours: Shirts - Red
Shorts - Red
Telephone No.: (01224) 632328
Ticket Information: (01224) 632328
Pitch Size: 109 × 71yds
Ground Capacity: 21,634 (all seats)

GENERAL INFORMATION
Supporters Club Administrator:
Susan Scott
Address: Aldon, Wellington Road, Aberdeen, AB1 4BJ
Telephone Number: (01224) 898260
Car Parking: Beach Boulevard, King Street & Golf Road
Coach Parking: Beach Boulevard
Nearest Railway Station: Aberdeen (1 mile)
Nearest Bus Station: Aberdeen
Club Shop: Crombie Sports, Bridge Street, Aberdeen
Opening Times: 9.00-5.30pm
Telephone No.: (01224) 593866
Postal Sales: Yes
Nearest Police Station: Aberdeen
Police Force: Grampian Police
Police Telephone No.: (01224) 639111

GROUND INFORMATION
Away Supporters' Entrances: Park Road
Away Supporters' Sections: South Stand East

DISABLED INFORMATION
Wheelchairs: 28 spaces in front of Richard Donald Stand & Merkland Stand
Disabled Toilets: 1 in Richard Donald Stand, 1 by Merkland Stand
The Blind: Special facilities may be available
Contact Nº: (01224) 632328 (Bookings necessary)

ADMISSION INFO (1996/97 PRICES)
Adult Seating: £10.00 - £17.00
Child Seating: £4.50 - £17.00
Family Section: £4.50 per child in the Family Section
Programme Price: £1.00
FAX Number: (01224) 644173

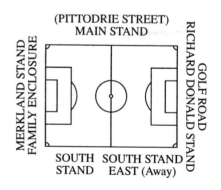

Travelling Supporters Information:
Routes: From City Centre travel along Union Street then turn left into King Street. Stadium is about 0.5 mile along King Street (A92) on the right.

AIRDRIEONIANS FC

Founded: 1878
Admitted to League: 1903
Former Name(s): Excelsior
Nickname: 'Diamonds' 'Waysiders'
Ground: Broadwood Stadium, Cumbernauld, Glasgow G67
Record Attendance: 6,200 (vs Hamilton 5/2/94)

Colours: Shirts - Red with White Diamond
Shorts - White
Telephone No.: (01236) 762067
Ticket Information: (01236) 747255
Pitch Size: 115 × 75yds
Ground Capacity: 6,230 (all seats)
Correspondence Address: 32 Stirling Street, Airdrie ML6 4DX

GENERAL INFORMATION

Supporters Club Administrator: David Johnstone
Address: 16 Deveron Street, Coatbridge
Telephone Number: (01236) 423812
Car Parking: Behind Main & West Stands
Coach Parking: Behind Main Stand
Nearest Railway Station: Croy (1.5 miles)
Nearest Bus Station: Cumbernauld Town Centre
Club Shop: Yes - at Ground
Opening Times: One hour before game
Telephone No.: (01236) 451511
Postal Sales: Yes
Nearest Police Station: South Muirhead Street, Cumbernauld
Police Force: Strathclyde
Police Telephone No.: (01236) 736085

Note: Airdrieonians are groundsharing with Clyde FC for the 1996/97 season.

GROUND INFORMATION
Away Supporters' Entrances: West Stand Turnstiles
Away Supporters' Sections: West Stand

DISABLED INFORMATION
Wheelchairs: 10 spaces each for home and away fans accommodated in the front sections of both stands
Disabled Toilets: 4 available in Main & West Stands
The Blind: No Special Facilities
Contact N°: (01236) 762067

ADMISSION INFO (1996/97 PRICES)
Adult Seating: £9.00
Child Seating: £5.00
Programme Price: £1.00
FAX Number: (01236) 760698

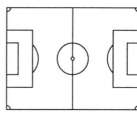

CAR PARK
WEST STAND

MAIN STAND
CAR PARK

Travelling Supporters Information:
Routes: From East: Exit A80 at Auchenkilns roundabout and follow signs for Broadwood Stadium. From West: Exit A80 at Broadwood Junction and follow signs for Broadwood Stadium.

ALBION ROVERS FC

Founded: 1882
Admitted to League: 1903
Former Name(s): None
Nickname: 'Wee Rovers'
Ground: Cliftonhill Stadium, Main Street, Coatbridge, Lanarkshire ML5 3RB
Record Attendance: 27,381 (8/2/36)

Colours: Shirts - Yellow with Red Trim
Shorts - Yellow
Telephone No.: (01236) 606334
Ticket Information: (01236) 606334
Pitch Size: 110 × 74yds
Ground Capacity: 1,238
Seating Capacity: 538

GENERAL INFORMATION

Supporters Club Administrator: None
Address: -
Telephone Number: -
Car Parking: Street Parking, Albion Street
Coach Parking: Albion Street
Nearest Railway Station: Coatdyke (10 mins walk)
Nearest Bus Station: Coatbridge
Club Shop: At Ground
Opening Times: One hour before each home match
Telephone No.: (01236) 606334
Postal Sales: Yes
Nearest Police Station: Coatbridge (0.5 mile)
Police Force: Coatbridge
Police Telephone No.: (01236) 420155

GROUND INFORMATION

Away Supporters' Entrances: Main Street Entrance
Away Supporters' Sections: Main Street Area

DISABLED INFORMATION

Wheelchairs: Approximately 30 spaces available in the Disabled Area
Disabled Toilets: One at the East End of the ground
The Blind: No Special Facilities
Contact Nº: (01236) 606334 (Bookings preferred)

ADMISSION INFO (1996/97 PRICES)

Adult Standing: £6.00
Adult Seating: £7.00
Child Standing: £3.00
Child Seating: £4.00
Programme Price: £1.00
FAX Number: (01236) 427192

```
        CAR PARK          Disabled
     ALBION STREET          Area

  W                            E
  E                            A
  S                            S
  T                            T
                              
  E                            E
  N                            N
  D                            D

        (Away)
      GRANDSTAND
      MAIN STREET
```

Travelling Supporters Information:
Routes: From East or West: Take the A8/M8 to the Shawhead Interchange then follow the A725 to the Town Centre. Take A89 signs towards Airdrie at the roundabout, the ground is then on the left; From the South: Take the A725 from Bellshill/Hamilton/Motherwell/M74 to Coatbridge. Take A89 signs towards Airdrie at the roundabout, the ground is then on the left; From North: Take A73 to Airdrie then follow signs for A8010 to Coatbridge. Join the A89 and the ground is one mile on the right.

ALLOA ATHLETIC FC

Founded: 1883
Admitted to League: 1921
Former Name(s): None
Nickname: 'The Wasps'
Ground: Recreation Park, Clackmannan Road, Alloa   FK10 1RR
Record Attendance: 13,000 (26/2/39)

Colours: Shirts - Gold & Black
Shorts - Black
Telephone No.: (01259) 722695
Ticket Information: (01259) 722695
Pitch Size: 110 × 75yds
Ground Capacity: 4,100
Seating Capacity: 424

GENERAL INFORMATION
Supporters Club Administrator:
R. Snaddon
Address: c/o Club
Telephone Number: (01259) 722695
Car Parking: Car Park Adjacent to Ground
Coach Parking: By Police Direction
Nearest Railway Station: Stirling (7 miles)
Nearest Bus Station: Alloa
Club Shop: At Ground
Opening Times: Matchdays Only 1.30-5.00
Telephone No.: (01259) 722695
Postal Sales: Yes
Nearest Police Station: Alloa (0.5 mile)
Police Force: Stirling & Clackmannan
Police Telephone No.: (01259) 723255

GROUND INFORMATION
Away Supporters' Entrances: Hilton Road
Away Supporters' Sections: Hilton Road Side and Clackmannan Road End

DISABLED INFORMATION
Wheelchairs: Accommodated in the Disabled Section underneath the Main Stand
Disabled Toilets: 1 available underneath Main Stand
Contact Nº: (01259) 722695

ADMISSION INFO (1996/97 PRICES)
Adult Standing: £6.00
Adult Seating: £7.00
Child Standing: £3.50
Child Seating: £3.50
Programme Price: £1.00
FAX Number: (01259) 722695

Travelling Supporters Information:
Routes: From South & East: Take M74 to M80 and exit at junction 9 following the A907 into Alloa. Continue over two roundabouts passing the brewery and Town Centre. The Ground is on the left-hand side of the road.

ARBROATH FC

Founded: 1878	**Colours**: Shirts - Maroon w/ White & Sky Blue
Admitted to League: 1902	Shorts - White with Maroon Trim
Former Name(s): None	**Telephone No.**: (01241) 872157
Nickname: 'The Red Lichties'	**Ticket Information**: (01241) 872157
Ground: Gayfield Park, Arbroath DD11 1QB	**Pitch Size**: 115 × 71yds
Record Attendance: 13,510 (23/2/52)	**Ground Capacity**: 6,488
	Seating Capacity: 715

GENERAL INFORMATION
Supporters Club Administrator: E. Ritchie
Address: 16 Beechwood Road, Arbroath DD11
Telephone Number: (01241) 878919
Car Parking: Car Park - Queen's Drive
Coach Parking: Car Park - Queen's Drive
Nearest Railway Station: Arbroath (15 mins walk)
Nearest Bus Station: Arbroath (10 minutes walk)
Club Shop: Premier Sports, West Port, Arbroath
Opening Times: Monday to Saturday 9.00am - 5.00pm
Telephone No.: (01241) 872838
Postal Sales: Yes
Nearest Police Station: Arbroath
Police Force: Tayside
Police Telephone No.: (01241) 872222

GROUND INFORMATION
Away Supporters' Entrances: None Specifically
Away Supporters' Sections: None unless an all ticket game then Queen's Drive End

DISABLED INFORMATION
Wheelchairs: 10 spaces available at the West End of the Main Stand
Disabled Toilets: One available by the club shop
Contact Nº: (01241) 872157

ADMISSION INFO (1996/97 PRICES)
Adult Standing: £6.00
Adult Seating: £7.00
Child Standing: £3.00
Child Seating: £3.50
Programme Price: £1.00
FAX Number: (01241) 872157

QUEEN'S DRIVE DUNDEE ROAD

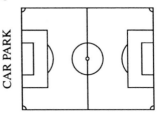

CAR PARK

Travelling Supporters Information:
Routes: From Dundee & the West: Take A92 (Coast Road), on entering Arbroath pass under railway line - Ground on right; From Stonehaven/Montrose: Take A92 (Coast Road), pass through Arbroath, past harbour - Ground on left.

AYR UNITED FC

Founded: 1910	**Record Attendance**: 25,225 (13/9/69)
Admitted to League: 1910	**Colours**: Shirts - Black
Former Name(s): Ayr Parkhouse & Ayr FC	Shorts - Black
(Amalgamated in 1910)	**Telephone No.**: (01292) 263435
Nickname: 'The Honest Men'	**Ticket Information**: (01292) 263435
Ground: Somerset Park, Tryfield Place, Ayr,	**Pitch Size**: 110 × 72yds
KA8 9NB	**Ground Capacity**: 13,918
	Seating Capacity: 1,450

GENERAL INFORMATION
Supporters Club Administrator: c/o Club
Address: -
Telephone Number: -
Car Parking: Craigie Car Park, Ayr Racecourse & Somerset Road Car Park
Coach Parking: Craigie Car Park
Nearest Railway Station: Ayr or Newton-on-Ayr (both 10 minutes walk)
Nearest Bus Station: Sandgate, Ayr
Club Shop: Ayr United Enterprises at ground
Opening Times: Weekdays 8.30am-5.30pm
Matchdays 1.00-3.00pm
Postal Sales: Yes
Nearest Police Station: King Street, Ayr (0.5 mile)
Police Force: Strathclyde
Police Telephone No.: (01292) 266966

GROUND INFORMATION
Away Supporters' Entrances: Railway End
Away Supporters' Sections: Railway End (Covered)

DISABLED INFORMATION
Wheelchairs: 30 spaces in the Disabled Area beneath the Family Stand
Disabled Toilets: 2 Gents & 1 Ladies in Disabled Area
The Blind: Commentary may be available (phone)
Contact Nº: (01292) 263435

ADMISSION INFO (1996/97 PRICES)
Adult Standing: £6.00
Adult Seating: £9.00
Child Standing: £3.00
Child Seating: Family Stand - Adult + 1 Child = £8.00
Programme Price: £1.00
FAX Number: (01292) 281314

SEGREGATION FENCE

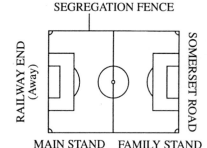

MAIN STAND   FAMILY STAND
TRYFIELD ROAD   (DISABLED)

Travelling Supporters Information:
Routes: Make for A77 Ring Road around Ayr, exit via Whitletts Roundabout onto the A719 and follow road towards Ayr. Just past the end of the racecourse, turn right at traffic lights into Burnett Terrace, sharp left and right takes you into Somerset Road. (For car parking on Matchdays turn left at traffic lights and then right 50 yards on into Craigie Park).

BERWICK RANGERS FC

Founded: 1881	**Colours**: Shirts - Black with Gold Diamonds,
Admitted to League: 1951	Pinstripes & Trim
Former Name(s): None	Shorts - Black with Gold Piping
Nickname: 'The Borderers'	**Telephone No.**: (01289) 307424
Ground: Shielfield Park, Shielfield Terrace,	**Pitch Size**: 112 × 76yds
Tweedmouth, Berwick-upon-Tweed TD15 2EF	**Ground Capacity**: 4,131
Record Attendance: 13,365 (28/1/67)	**Seating Capacity**: 1,366

GENERAL INFORMATION
Supporters Club Administrator: Gordon Dickson
Address: 19 Greenwood, Tweedmouth, Berwick-Upon-Tweed
Telephone Number: (01289) 308317
Car Parking: Large Car Park at Ground
Coach Parking: Car Park at Ground
Nearest Railway Station: Berwick-upon-Tweed
Nearest Bus Station: Town Centre, Berwick-upon-Tweed
Club Shop: Supporters' Club in Ground
Opening Times: Matchdays Only
Telephone No.: via the Club
Postal Sales: Yes - via Supporters' Club at Ground
Nearest Police Station: Berwick-upon-Tweed - Church Street (1 mile)
Police Force: Northumbria
Police Telephone No.: (01289) 307111

GROUND INFORMATION
Away Supporters' Entrances: Shielfield Terrace
Away Supporters' Sections: Popular Side Terracing

DISABLED INFORMATION
Wheelchairs: Accommodated in the Main Stand
Disabled Toilets: Available in General Toilet Block
Contact N°: (01289) 307424 or 307623 (Bookings are necessary)

ADMISSION INFO (1996/97 PRICES)
Adult Standing: £6.00
Adult Seating: £7.00
Child Standing: £3.00
Child Seating: £3.00
Programme Price: £1.00
FAX Number: (01289) 307623 (Secretary's Number)
(01289) 307424 (Ground Number)

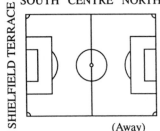

Travelling Supporters Information:
Routes: From North: Take A1 (Berwick Bypass), cross new road-bridge then at roundabout take 1st exit. Carry on for approximately 0.25 mile to the next roundabout, go straight across then continue approximately 0.25 mile into Shielfield Terrace. Turn left and the ground is on the left; From South: Take A1 Bypass, at junction take 'Spittal' Road (right) and continue for approximately 1 mile until the road become Shielfield Terrace. Ground is on the left.

BRECHIN CITY FC

Founded: 1906
Admitted to League: 1923
Former Name(s): None
Nickname: 'The City'
Ground: Glebe Park, Trinity Road, Brechin, Angus   DD9 6BJ
Record Attendance: 8,244 (3/2/73)

Colours: Shirts - Red & White
Shorts - Red & White
Telephone No.: (01356) 622856
Ticket Information: (01356) 622856
Pitch Size: 110 × 76yds
Ground Capacity: 3,900
Seating Capacity: 1,518

GENERAL INFORMATION
Supporters Club Administrator:
Rick Robertson
Address: c/o Glebe Park
Telephone Number: -
Car Parking: Small Car Park at Ground & Street Parking
Coach Parking: Street Parking
Nearest Railway Station: Montrose (8 miles)
Nearest Bus Station: Brechin
Club Shop: At Ground
Opening Times: Matchdays Only
Telephone No.: (01356) 622856
Postal Sales: Yes
Nearest Police Station: Brechin (400 yards)
Police Force: Tayside
Police Telephone No.: (01356) 622222

GROUND INFORMATION
Away Supporters' Entrances: None Specifically
Away Supporters' Sections: None Specifically

DISABLED INFORMATION
Wheelchairs: 10 spaces each for home & away fans accommodated in front of the Seated Enclosure
Disabled Toilets: 2 available in the Covered Enclosure
Contact Nº: (01356) 622942 (Bookings necessary)

ADMISSION INFO (1996/97 PRICES)
Adult Standing: £6.00
Adult Seating: £7.00 - £8.00
Child Standing: £3.00
Child Seating: £3.00 - £4.00
Programme Price: £1.00
FAX Number: (01356) 622942

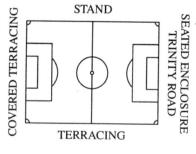

STAND

COVERED TERRACING

SEATED ENCLOSURE
TRINITY ROAD

TERRACING

Travelling Supporters Information:
Routes: From South & West: Take M90 to A94 and continue along past first 'Brechin' turn-off and take second turn signposted 'Brechin'. On entering Brechin, ground is on left of road, between houses.

CELTIC FC

Founded: 1888
Admitted to League: 1890 (Founder Member)
Former Name(s): None
Nickname: 'The Bhoys'
Ground: Celtic Park, 95 Kerrydale Street, Glasgow G40 3RE
Record Attendance: 92,000 (1/1/38)
Colours: Shirts - Green & White Hoops Shorts - White
Telephone No.: (0141) 556-2611
Ticket Information: (0141) 551-8653
Pitch Size: 114 × 75yds
Ground Capacity: 47,000 (all seats)

GENERAL INFORMATION
Supporters Club Administrator: -
Address: Celtic Supporters' Association, Barrowfield Ground, 1524 London Road, Glasgow, G40 3RJ
Telephone Number: (0141) 554-6250
Car Parking: In front of the Main Stand. Also Adjacent to the Ground
Coach Parking: Adjacent to the Ground
Nearest Railway Station: Bridgeton Cross (10 minutes walk)
Club Shop: Shop at Celtic Park. Also Celtic Shops, 40 Dundas St., Glasgow & 21 High St.
Opening Times: At Ground: Weekdays & Matchdays 9.30am-4.30pm; At Dundas Street & High St.: Monday to Saturday 9.00-5.00pm
Telephone No.: (0141) 554-4231 (At Ground) (0141) 332-2727 (Dundas Street)
Postal Sales: Yes
Nearest Police Station: London Road, Glasgow (0.3 mile)
Police Force: Strathclyde
Police Telephone No.: (0141) 532) 4600

GROUND INFORMATION
Away Supporters' Entrances: Kinloch St. Turnstiles
Away Supporters' Sections: East Stand

DISABLED INFORMATION
Wheelchairs: 96 spaces for home fans and 10 spaces for away fans in the North Stand and East Stand
Disabled Toilets: 5 available in the North Stand and 2 in the East Stand
The Blind: Contact the club for details of facilities
Contact N°: (0141) 556-2611 (Bookings necessary)

ADMISSION INFO (1996/97 PRICES)
Adult Seating: £9.00 - £19.00
Child Seating: £5.00 - £19.00
Programme Price: £1.00
FAX Number: (041) 551-8106
Note: Prices vary according to the category of match and position in the ground.

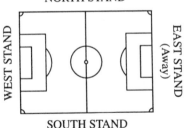

(JANEFIELD STREET)
NORTH STAND

WEST STAND

EAST STAND (Away)

SOUTH STAND
LONDON ROAD

Travelling Supporters Information:
Routes: From the South & East: Take A74 London Road towards the City Centre, Kerrydale Street is on the right about 0.25 mile past the Belvidere Hospital and the ground is clearly visible; From the West: Take A74 London Road from the City Centre and turn left about 0.5 mile past Bridgeton Central Station.

CLYDE FC

Founded: 1878
Admitted to League: 1906
Former Name(s): None
Nickname: 'Bully Wee'
Ground: Broadwood Stadium, Cumbernauld, Glasgow G67
Record Attendance: 6,200 (vs Hamilton 5/2/94)

Colours: Shirts - White with Red & Black
Shorts - Black
Telephone No.: (01236) 451511
Ticket Information: (01236) 451511
Pitch Size: 115 × 75yds
Ground Capacity: 8,000 (all seats)
Correspondence Address: 219 St. Vincent Street, Glasgow G2 5QY

GENERAL INFORMATION
Supporters Club Administrator: None
Address: -
Telephone Number: -
Car Parking: Behind Main & West Stands
Coach Parking: Behind Main Stand
Nearest Railway Station: Croy (1.5 miles)
Nearest Bus Station: Cumbernauld Town Centre
Club Shop: Yes - at Ground
Opening Times: One hour before game and after the game
Telephone No.: (01236) 451511
Postal Sales: Yes
Nearest Police Station: South Muirhead Street, Cumbernauld
Police Force: Strathclyde
Police Telephone No.: (01236) 736085

GROUND INFORMATION
Away Supporters' Entrances: West Stand Turnstiles
Away Supporters' Sections: West Stand

DISABLED INFORMATION
Wheelchairs: 10 spaces each for home & away fans accommodated in the front sections of each stand
Disabled Toilets: 4 available in Main & West Stands
Contact Nº: (01236) 451511

ADMISSION INFO (1996/97 PRICES)
Adult Seating: £8.00
Child Seating: £4.00
Programme Price: £1.50
FAX Number: (01236) 733490
Family Ticket = 1 Adult + 1 Child £10.00

WEST STAND

MAIN STAND

Travelling Supporters Information:
Routes: From East: Exit A80 at Auchenkilns Roundabout and follow signs for the Broadwood Stadium.
From West: Exit A80 at Broadwood Junction and follow signs for Broadwood Stadium.

CLYDEBANK FC

Founded: 1965
Admitted to League: 1966
Former Name(s): None
Nickname: 'The Bankies'
Ground: Boghead Park, Miller Street,
Dumbarton, Glasgow   G82 2JA
Record Attendance: 18,000 (2/3/57)
Office Address: c/o West of Scotland RFC,
Burn Brae, Milngabie, Glasgow   G62 6HX

Colours: Shirts - White with Red & Black
Shorts - White with Black & Red
Telephone No.: (0141) 955-9048
Ticket Information: (0141) 955-9048
Pitch Size: 110 × 68yds
Ground Capacity: 7,503
Seating Capacity: 303

Clydebank are groundsharing with Dumbarton during
the 1996/97 season

GENERAL INFORMATION
Supporters Club Official: c/o Club
Address: –
Telephone Number: –
Car Parking: Street Parking
Coach Parking: Dumbarton Common
Nearest Railway Station: Dumbarton (East)
(10 minutes walk)
Nearest Bus Station: Dumbarton
Club Shop: c/o Office
Opening Times: Office Hours
Telephone No.: (0141) 955-9048
Postal Sales: Yes
Nearest Police Station: Dumbarton
Police Force: Strathclyde
Police Telephone No.: (01389) 763311

GROUND INFORMATION
Away Supporters' Entrances: Boghead Av. turnstiles
Away Supporters' Sections: Boghead Avenue End

DISABLED INFORMATION
Wheelchairs: 3 pitchside spaces for home fans only
Disabled Toilets: None
Contact Nº: (01389) 762569 (Bookings necessary)

ADMISSION INFO (1995/96 PRICES)
Adult Standing: £8.00
Adult Seating: £10.00
Child Standing: £4.00
Child Seating: £6.00
Programme Price: £1.00
FAX Number: (0141) 955-9049

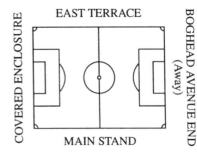

Travelling Supporters Information:
Routes: From All Parts: Exit M8 at Junction 17 and take A82 to Dumbarton. Follow signs for 'Loch Lomond' along dual carriageway and take left turn before B.P. Garage at traffic lights. Home entrance is then 2nd on left. Away supporters take left turn at Dunbritton Road (before B.P. Garage) and follow signs to Silverton area. Then walk to Boghead Avenue turnstiles.

COWDENBEATH FC

Founded: 1881	**Colours**: Shirts - Royal Blue with White & Red
Admitted to League: 1921	Shorts - Royal Blue with White & Red
Former Name(s): The Miners	**Telephone No.**: (01383) 610166
Nickname: 'Cowden' / 'Blue Brazil'	**Ticket Information**: (01383) 610166
Ground: Central Park, High Street,	**Pitch Size**: 107 × 66yds
Cowdenbeath KY4 9EY	**Ground Capacity**: 5,258
Record Attendance: 25,586 (21/4/49)	**Seating Capacity**: 1,552

GENERAL INFORMATION
Supporters Club Administrator: W. Nellies
Address: c/o Club
Telephone Number: (01383) 610166
Car Parking: Car Park at Ground being upgraded and Stenhouse Street (200 yards)
Coach Parking: King St. and Rowan Terrace
Nearest Railway Station: Cowdenbeath (400 yards)
Nearest Bus Station: Cowdenbeath (Bus Stop at Ground)
Club Shop: At Ground
Opening Times: 10.00am - 3.00pm Monday to Friday; 1.00am - 3.00pm Saturdays
Telephone No.: (01383) 610166
Postal Sales: Yes
Nearest Police Station: Cowdenbeath (300 yards)
Police Force: Fife
Police Telephone No.: (01383) 318600

GROUND INFORMATION
Away Supporters' Entrances: Main Entrance
Away Supporters' Sections: South & East Sides

DISABLED INFORMATION
Wheelchairs: 3 spaces each for home & away fans
Disabled Toilets: 1 Ladies, 1 Gents & 1 Communal
Contact Nº: (01383) 610166 (Bookings necessary)

ADMISSION INFO (1996/97 PRICES)
Adult Standing: £5.00
Adult Seating: £6.00
Child Standing: £2.50
Child Seating: £3.00
Programme Price: 80p
FAX Number: (01383) 512132

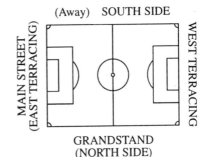

Travelling Supporters Information:
Routes: Exit M90 at Junction 3 for Dunfermline. Take Dual Carriageway to Cowdenbeath and follow straight on into the High Street. Ground is situated on the first left turn in the High Street.

DUMBARTON FC

Founded: 1872
Admitted to League: 1890 (Founder Member)
Former Name(s): None
Nickname: 'Sons'
Ground: Boghead Park, Miller Street,
Dumbarton   G82 2JA
Record Attendance: 18,000 (2/3/57)

Colours: Shirts - Gold with Black Trim
Shorts - Black
Telephone No.: (01389) 762569
Ticket Information: (01389) 762569
Pitch Size: 110 × 68yds
Ground Capacity: 7,503
Seating Capacity: 303

GENERAL INFORMATION
Supporters Club Administrator: -
Address: c/o Club
Telephone Number: -
Car Parking: Street Parking
Coach Parking: Dumbarton Common
Nearest Railway Station: Dumbarton (East) -
(10 minute walk)
Nearest Bus Station: Dumbarton
Club Shop: Yes - at Ground
Opening Times: Matchdays & Weekdays
10.00am - 1.00pm
Telephone No.: (01389) 762569
Postal Sales: Yes - c/o Club
Nearest Police Station: Dumbarton
Police Force: Strathclyde
Police Telephone No.: (01389) 763311

GROUND INFORMATION
Away Supporters' Entrances: Boghead Avenue
Away Supporters' Sections: Boghead Avenue
Covered Enclosure

DISABLED INFORMATION
Wheelchairs: 3 trackside spaces for home fans only
Disabled Toilets: One available in the Main Stand
Contact Nº: (01389) 762569

ADMISSION INFO (1996/97 PRICES)
Adult Standing: £7.00
Adult Seating: £8.50
Child Standing: £3.50
Child Seating: £4.50
Programme Price: £1.00
FAX Number: (01389) 762629

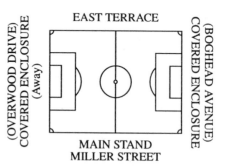

Travelling Supporters Information:
Routes: From All Parts: Exit M8 at Junction 17 and take A82 to Dumbarton. Follow signs for 'Loch Lomond' along dual carriageway and take left turn before B.P. Garage at traffic lights. Home entrance is then 2nd on left. Away supporters take left turn at Dunbritton Road (before B.P. Garage) and follow signs to Silverton area. Then walk to Boghead Avenue turnstiles.

DUNDEE FC

Founded: 1893	**Colours**: Shirts - Blue
Admitted to League: 1893	Shorts - White
Former Name(s): None	**Telephone No.**: (01382) 826104
Nickname: 'The Dark Blues'	**Ticket Information**: (01382) 826104
Ground: Dens Park Stadium, Dens Road,	**Pitch Size**: 113 × 73yds
Dundee DD3 7JY	**Ground Capacity**: 13,977
Record Attendance: 43,024 (7/2/53)	**Seating Capacity**: 10,677

GENERAL INFORMATION

Supporters Club Administrator: S. Martin
Address: c/o Club
Telephone Number: (01382) 826104
Car Parking: Private 600 space car park
Coach Parking: 50 yards from Ground
Nearest Railway Station: Dundee
Nearest Bus Station: Dundee
Club Shop:
Opening Times: 9.00-5.30pm Weekdays
Telephone No.: (01382) 826104
Postal Sales: Yes
Nearest Police Station: Bell Street, Dundee
Police Force: Tayside
Police Telephone No.: (01382) 23200

GROUND INFORMATION

Away Supporters' Entrances: Provost Road
Away Supporters' Sections: West Terracing

DISABLED INFORMATION

Wheelchairs: Accommodated in the Family Stand
Disabled Toilets: Adjacent to the Family Stand
Contact Nº: (01382) 826104 (Bookings necessary)

ADMISSION INFO (1996/97 PRICES)

Adult Standing: £8.00
Adult Seating: £8.00 - £10.00
Child Standing: £4.00
Child Seating: £4.00 - £5.00
Programme Price: £1.00
FAX Number: (01382) 832284
Note: The Family Section has special rates.

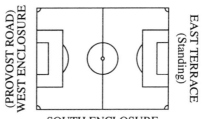

CENTRE STAND
(FAMILY SECTION)
SANDEMAN STREET   TANNADICE STREET
(PROVOST ROAD)
WEST ENCLOSURE
EAST TERRACE (Standing)
SOUTH ENCLOSURE
(DENS ROAD)

Travelling Supporters Information:
Routes: Take A972 from Perth (Kingsway West) to Kings Cross Circus Roundabout. Take 3rd exit into Clepington Road and turn right into Provost Road (1 mile) then 2nd left into Sandeman Street for ground.

DUNDEE UNITED FC

Founded: 1909
Admitted to League: 1910
Former Name(s): Dundee Hibernians
Nickname: 'The Terrors'
Ground: Tannadice Park, Tannadice Street, Dundee   DD3 7JW
Record Attendance: 28,000 (Nov. 1966)

Colours: Shirts - Tangerine
Shorts - Black
Telephone No.: (01382) 833166
Ticket Information: (01382) 833166
Pitch Size: 110 × 72yds
Ground Capacity: 12,608 (all seats)

GENERAL INFORMATION

Supporters Club Administrator:
James Gardiner
Address: 51 Silverknowes Drive, Edinburgh, EH45 5HH
Telephone Number: (0131) 336-4049
Car Parking: Street Parking & Gussie Park
Coach Parking: Gussie Park (100 yards)
Nearest Railway Station: Dundee
Nearest Bus Station: Dundee
Club Shop: At ground on Matchdays Only or 5 Victoria Street, Dundee
Opening Times: At Ground: Matchdays 2.00pm - 5.00pm; At Victoria Road: 9.00am - 5.30pm
Telephone No.: (01382) 833166
Postal Sales: Yes
Nearest Police Station: Bell Street, Dundee
Police Force: Tayside
Police Telephone No.: (01382) 22320

GROUND INFORMATION

Away Supporters' Entrances: West Stand Turnstiles
Away Supporters' Sections: West Stand (for certain games)

DISABLED INFORMATION

Wheelchairs: Accommodated in George Fox Stand
Disabled Toilets: 2 available in the George Fox Stand
The Blind: Commentary may be available. Contact the club for further details
Contact Nº: (01382) 833166 (Bookings necessary)

ADMISSION INFO (1996/97 PRICES)

Adult Seating: £8.00 to £10.00
Child Seating: £4.00 or £6.00
Programme Price: £1.00
FAX Number: (01382) 89398
Note: Additional discounts available in Family Section

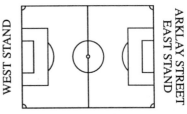

GEORGE FOX STAND

WEST STAND

ARKLAY STREET
EAST STAND

MAIN STAND
(TANNADICE STREET)

Travelling Supporters Information:
Routes: Take A972 from Perth (Kingsway West) to Kings Cross Circus Roundabout. Take 3rd exit into Clepington Road and turn right into Provost Road (1 mile) then 2nd left into Sandeman Street for ground.

DUNFERMLINE ATHLETIC FC

Founded: 1885
Admitted to League: 1921
Former Name(s): None
Nickname: 'The Pars'
Ground: East End Park, Halbeath Road, Dunfermline, Fife
Record Attendance: 27,816 (30/4/68)

Colours: Shirts - Black & White Stripes
Shorts - Black
Telephone No.: (01383) 724295
Ticket Information: (01383) 724295
Pitch Size: 115 × 68yds
Ground Capacity: 18,328
Seating Capacity: 4,008

GENERAL INFORMATION
Supporters Club Administrator:
Mrs J. Malcolm
Address: 15 Meadowfield, Cowdenbeath
Telephone Number: (01383) 610138
Car Parking: Street Parking, Car Park at Ground and Multistorey (10 minutes walk)
Coach Parking: Adjacent to Ground
Nearest Railway Station: Dunfermline (15 minutes walk)
Nearest Bus Station: Carnegie Drive, Dunfermline (10 minutes walk)
Club Shop: Intersport, Kingsgate, Dunfermline
Opening Times: Monday-Saturday 9.00-5.00pm
Telephone No.: (01383) 739980
Postal Sales: Yes
Nearest Police Station: Holyrood Place (10 minutes walk)
Police Force: Fife
Police Telephone No.: (01383) 726711

GROUND INFORMATION
Away Supporters' Entrances: Turnstiles 14-29
Away Supporters' Sections: East Terracing (Open) & North East Enclosure (Covered)

DISABLED INFORMATION
Wheelchairs: 15 spaces each for home & away fans
Disabled Toilets: One available in the West End Stand
The Blind: Free admission to the West End Stand
Contact Nº: (01383) 724295

ADMISSION INFO (1996/97 PRICES)
Adult Standing: £10.00
Adult Seating: £10.00 - £13.00
Child Standing: £5.00
Child Seating: £5.00 - £7.00
Programme Price: £1.20
FAX Number: (01383) 723468

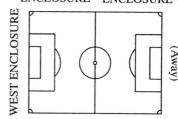

NORTH ENCLOSURE   NORTH EAST ENCLOSURE (Away)

WEST ENCLOSURE

EAST TERRACING (Away)

COMMUNITY ENCLOSURE   FAMILY ENCLOSURE

HALBEATH ROAD STAND

Travelling Supporters Information:
Routes: From Forth Road Bridge and Perth: Exit M90 Junction 3 and take A907 (Halbeath Road) into Dunfermline - Ground on right; From Kincardine Bridge and Alloa: Take A985 to A994 then into Dunfermline. Take Pittencrief Street, Glen Bridge and Carnegie Drive to Sinclair Gardens roundabout. Take 2nd exit into Appin Crescent and continue into Halbeath Road. Ground on left.

EAST FIFE FC

Founded: 1903
Admitted to League: 1903
Former Name(s): None
Nickname: 'The Fifers'
Ground: Bayview Park, Wellesley Road, Methil, Fifeshire   KY8 3AG
Record Attendance: 22,515 (2/1/50)

Colours: Shirts - Amber and Black Stripe
Shorts - Amber and Black
Telephone No.: (01333) 426323
Ticket Information: (01333) 426323
Pitch Size: 110×71yds
Ground Capacity: 5,385
Seating Capacity: 600

GENERAL INFORMATION
Supporters Club Administrator: M. McColl
Address: 60 Rothes Road, Glenrothes
Telephone Number: (01592) 757249
Car Parking: Adjacent to Ground
Coach Parking: Adjacent to Ground
Nearest Railway Station: Kirkcaldy (8 mls)
Nearest Bus Station: Leven
Club Shop: At Ground
Opening Times: Matchdays Only
Telephone No.: -
Postal Sales: Contact Office
Nearest Police Station: Sea Road, Methil (1 mile)
Police Force: Fife
Police Telephone No.: (01592) 712881

GROUND INFORMATION
Away Supporters' Entrances: School End
Away Supporters' Sections: School End
DISABLED INFORMATION
Wheelchairs: 20 spaces for home fans, 10 spaces for away fans accommodated at the end of the Grandstand
Disabled Toilets: 2 available behind the Grandstand
Contact Nº: (01333)426323 (Book 1 week in advance)

ADMISSION INFO (1996/97 PRICES)
Adult Standing: £8.00
Adult Seating: £9.00
Child Standing: £4.00
Child Seating: £5.00
Programme Price: £1.00
FAX Number: (01333) 426376

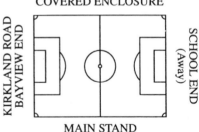

COVERED ENCLOSURE

KIRKLAND ROAD
BAYVIEW END

SCHOOL END
(Away)

MAIN STAND
WELLESLEY ROAD

Travelling Supporters Information:
Routes: From South: Take A90 Forth Road Bridge, then M90 and exit Junction 3 (Bells Roundabout). Take A92 to Kirkcaldy East then follow signs for Leven. Take right turn for Buckhaven just before Leven, then Lower Methil right turn. Ground is about 0.5 mile on left and floodlights are visible for 0.25 mile.

EAST STIRLINGSHIRE FC

Founded: 1880
Admitted to League: 1900
Former Name(s): Bainsford Britannia
Nickname: 'The Shire'
Ground: Firs Park, Firs Street, Falkirk
FK2 7AY
Record Attendance: 12,000 (21/2/21)

Colours: Shirts - Black & White Hoops
Shorts - Black
Telephone No.: (01324) 623583
Ticket Information: (01324) 623583
Pitch Size: 112 × 72yds
Ground Capacity: 1,880
Seating Capacity: 280

GENERAL INFORMATION

Supporters Club Administrator: None
Address: -
Telephone Number: -
Car Parking: Street Parking
Coach Parking: Street Parking
Nearest Railway Station: Grahamston (10 minutes walk)
Nearest Bus Station: Falkirk
Club Shop: At Ground
Opening Times: Weekdays (except Thursday) & Saturday Matchdays 10.00am - 2.30pm
Telephone No.: (01324) 623583
Postal Sales: Yes
Nearest Police Station: Falkirk (0.5 mile)
Police Force: Central Region
Police Telephone No.: (01324) 634212

GROUND INFORMATION

Away Supporters' Entrances: None Specifically
Away Supporters' Sections: None Specifically

DISABLED INFORMATION

Wheelchairs: Accommodation not specified
Disabled Toilets: Available in the Main Stand
Contact Nº: (01324) 623583 (Bookings necessary)

ADMISSION INFO (1996/97 PRICES)

Adult Standing: £5.00
Adult Seating: £6.00
Child Standing: £2.50
Child Seating: £3.00
Programme Price: £1.00
FAX Number: (01324) 637862

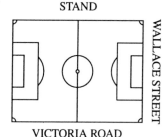

STAND

WALLACE STREET

VICTORIA ROAD

Travelling Supporters Information:
Routes: From Glasgow/Edinburgh: Exit Motorway at signs marked Grangemouth, follow AA signs for football traffic into Falkirk as far as Thornhill Road (where road meets 'Give Way' sign). Once in Thornhill Road turn left into Firs Street at St. James' Church. Ground straight ahead.

FALKIRK FC

Founded: 1876	**Colours**: Shirts - Navy Blue
Admitted to League: 1902	Shorts - White
Former Name(s): None	**Telephone No.**: (01324) 624121
Nickname: 'The Bairns'	**Ticket Information**: (01324) 624121
Ground: Brockville Park, Hope Street,	**Pitch Size**: 110 × 70yds
Falkirk, FK1 5AX	**Ground Capacity**: 12,000
Record Attendance: 23,100 (21/2/53)	**Seating Capacity**: 2,661

GENERAL INFORMATION
Supporters Club Administrator: None
Address: -
Telephone Number: -
Car Parking: Car Park at Ground (200 Cars)
& Town Car Park
Coach Parking: Town Car Park (100 yards)
Nearest Railway Station: Grahamston (100 yards)
Nearest Bus Station: Falkirk Centre (800 yards)
Club Shop: Glebe Street, Falkirk
Opening Times: 9.00am – 5.00pm
Telephone No.: (01324) 639366
Postal Sales: Yes
Nearest Police Station: Hope Street, Falkirk (0.5 mile)
Police Force: Central Scotland
Police Telephone No.: (01324) 634212

GROUND INFORMATION
Away Supporters' Entrances: James Street End
Away Supporters' Sections: James Street End

DISABLED INFORMATION
Wheelchairs: 14 spaces by the Watson Street side
Disabled Toilets: Yes
Contact N°: (01324) 624121 (Bookings necessary)

ADMISSION INFO (1996/97 PRICES)
Adult Standing: £8.00
Adult Seating: £8.50 or £10.00
Child Standing: £4.00
Child Seating: £5.00
Programme Price: £1.00
FAX Number: (01324) 612418

CAR PARK

STAND

HOPE STREET END

JAMES STREET END

COVERED ENCLOSURE
(Watson Street)

Travelling Supporters Information:
Routes: From North & West: Exit M876 Junction 1 and take A883 into A803 to Falkirk. Pass along Camelon Road and West Bridge Street and turn left into Hope Street by Police Station. Follow along over railway line for Ground (about half a mile); From South & East: Take A803 road from Linlithglow into Falkirk along Callendar Road. Pass Callendar Shopping Centre (on right) along High Street and turn right into Hope Street by Police Station (then as North & West).

FORFAR ATHLETIC FC

Founded: 1885	**Colours**: Shirts - Sky Blue with Navy Stripe
Admitted to League: 1921	Shorts - Navy Blue
Former Name(s): None	**Telephone No.**: (01307) 463576
Nickname: 'Loons'	**Ticket Information**: (01307) 463576
Ground: Station Park, Carseview Road,	**Pitch Size**: 115 × 69yds
Forfar, Tayside	**Ground Capacity**: 8,388
Record Attendance: 10,780 (2/2/70)	**Seating Capacity**: 739

GENERAL INFORMATION
Supporters Club Administrator:
Mrs. Y. Nicholl
Address: -
Telephone Number: (01307) 467255
Car Parking: Market Muir Car Park and adjacent Streets
Coach Parking: Market Muir Car Park
Nearest Railway Station: Dundee or Arbroath (both 14 miles)
Nearest Bus Station: Forfar (0.5 mile)
Club Shop: 45 East High Street, Forfar
Opening Times: Shopping Hours
Telephone No.: (01307) 465959
Postal Sales: Yes
Nearest Police Station: West High Street, Forfar
Police Force: Tayside
Police Telephone No.: (01307) 462551

GROUND INFORMATION
Away Supporters' Entrances: West End
Away Supporters' Sections: West End Terracing/
Main Stand (North)

DISABLED INFORMATION
Wheelchairs: 4 spaces each for home and away fans accommodated to the west of the Main Stand
Disabled Toilets: One available
Contact Nº: (01307) 463576

ADMISSION INFO (1996/97 PRICES)
Adult Standing: £5.00
Adult Seating: £5.50
Child Standing: £2.50
Child Seating: £2.50
Programme Price: 80p
FAX Number: None

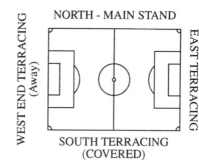

Travelling Supporters Information:
Routes: Take A85/M90 to Dundee and then A929 exit at 2nd turnoff (signposted Forfar). On the outskirts of Forfar, turn right at the T-junction and then left at the next major road. Ground is signposted on the left (cobbled street with railway arch).

GREENOCK MORTON FC

Founded: 1874
Admitted to League: 1893
Former Name(s): None
Nickname: 'Ton'
Ground: Cappielow Park, Sinclair Street, Greenock PA15 2TY
Record Attendance: 23,500 (29/4/21)

Colours: Shirts - Royal Blue Tartan
Shorts - Royal Blue
Telephone No.: (01475) 723571
Ticket Information: (01475) 723571
Pitch Size: 110 × 71yds
Ground Capacity: 14,267
Seating Capacity: 5,257

GENERAL INFORMATION
Supporters Club Administrator: J. Crawford
Address: Regent Street, Greenock
Telephone Number: (01475) 721081
Car Parking: James Watt Dock
Coach Parking: James Watt Dock
Nearest Railway Station: Cartsdyke (0.5 ml)
Nearest Bus Station: Town Centre (1.5 mile)
Club Shop: Yes - inside Ground
Opening Times: Matchdays Only
Telephone No.: None
Postal Sales: Yes
Nearest Police Station: Rue End Street, Greenock
Police Force: Strathclyde
Police Telephone No.: (01475) 724444

GROUND INFORMATION
Away Supporters' Entrances: East Hamilton Street Turnstiles
Away Supporters' Sections: East Hamilton Street

DISABLED INFORMATION
Wheelchairs: 5 spaces each for home and away fans accommodated below the Grandstand
Disabled Toilets: None
The Blind: Commentaries may be available. Contact the club for further details
Contact Nº: (01475) 723571

ADMISSION INFO (1996/97 PRICES)
Adult Standing: £8.00
Adult Seating: £10.00
Child Standing: £4.00
Child Seating: £5.00
Programme Price: £1.00
FAX Number: (01475) 781084
Note: Family Discounts are available

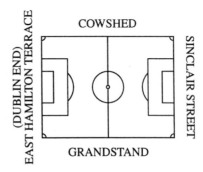

Travelling Supporters Information:
Routes: From All Parts: Take M8 to A8. Pass through Port Glasgow and turn left after passing dockyard buildings on the right-hand side of the road.

HAMILTON ACADEMICAL FC

Founded: 1874
Admitted to League: 1897
Former Name(s): None
Nickname: 'The Accies'
Ground: Cliftonhill Stadium, Main Street, Coatbridge, Lanarkshire   ML5 3RB
Record Attendance: 49,838 (18/2/22)
Note: The Club is currently Groundsharing with Albion Rovers FC

Correspondence Address: Douglas Park, Douglas Park Lane, Hamilton   ML3 0DF
Colours: Shirts - Red and White Hoops
         Shorts - White with Red Flash
Telephone No.: (01698) 286103
Pitch Size: 110 × 74yds
Ground Capacity: 1,238
Seating Capacity: 538

GENERAL INFORMATION
Supporters Club Administrator: W.McLachlan
Address: c/o Hamilton Academical Supporters Club, 51 Burnbank Road, Hamilton
Telephone Number: (01698) 284603
Car Parking: Street Parking
Coach Parking: Albion Street
Nearest Railway Station: Coatdyke (10 minutes walk)
Nearest Bus Station: Coatbridge
Club Shop: Contact Club Office At Douglas Park
Opening Times: Office Hours
Telephone No.: (01698) 286103
Postal Sales: Yes
Nearest Police Station: Coatbridge (0.5 mile)
Police Force: Strathclyde
Police Telephone No.: (01236) 420155

GROUND INFORMATION
Away Supporters' Entrances: Main Street Entrance
Away Supporters' Sections: Main Street Side

DISABLED INFORMATION
Wheelchairs: Approximately 30 spaces available in the Disabled Section.
Disabled Toilets: One available at the East End of the ground
Contact N°: (01236) 606334 (Bookings preferred)

ADMISSION INFO (1996/97 PRICES)
Adult Seating: £7.00
Child Seating: £4.00
Programme Price: £1.00
FAX Number: (01698) 285422
Note: The Club will be moving to a New Stadium for the 1997/98 Season

Travelling Supporters Information:
Routes: From East or West: Take the A8/M8 to the Shawhead Interchange then follow the A725 to the Town Centre. Take A89 signs towards Airdrie at the roundabout, the ground is then on the left; From the South: Take the A725 from Bellshill/Hamilton/Motherwell/M74 to Coatbridge. Take A89 signs towards Airdrie at the roundabout, the ground is then on the left; From North: Take A73 to Airdrie then follow signs for A8010 to Coatbridge. Join the A89 and the ground is one mile on the right.

HEART OF MIDLOTHIAN FC

Founded: 1874
Admitted to League: 1890 (Founder Member)
Former Name(s): None
Nickname: 'The Jam Tarts'
Ground: Tynecastle Park, Gorgie Road,
Edinburgh   EH11 2NL
Record Attendance: 53,496 (13/1/32)

Colours: Shirts - Maroon
    Shorts - White
Telephone No.: (0131) 337-6132
Ticket Information: (0131) 337-9011
Pitch Size: 110 × 74yds
Ground Capacity: 16,613 approx. (all seats)

GENERAL INFORMATION
Supporters Club Administrator:
J.N. Borthwick
Address: 80 Slateford Road, Edinburgh,
EH11 1QU
Telephone Number: (0131) 539-2574
Car Parking: Street Parking in Robertson
Avenue & Westfield Road
Coach Parking: Chesser Avenue
Nearest Railway Station: Edinburgh Haymarket (0.5 mile)
Nearest Bus Station: St. Andrew's Square
Club Shop: Adjacent to ground
Opening Times: Weekdays 9.30-5.00pm and
Matchdays 10.00-5.00pm
Telephone No.: (0131) 346-8511
Postal Sales: Yes
Nearest Police Station: Haymarket,
Edinburgh
Police Force: Lothian & Borders
Police Telephone No.: (0131) 229-2323

GROUND INFORMATION
Away Supporters' Entrances: Check with club
Away Supporters' Sections: -

DISABLED INFORMATION
Wheelchairs: 22 spaces for home fans in the School
End Stand. 8 spaces for away fans in the South Enclosure
Disabled Toilets: 2 available in the South Enclosure
The Blind: Commentary may be available. Contact Club
Contact Nº: (0131) 337-6132 (Bookings necessary)

ADMISSION INFO (1995/96 PRICES)
Adult Seating: £9.00 - £13.00
Child Seating: £5.00 (Family Area)
Programme Price: £1.00
FAX Number: (0131) 346-0699

WHEATFIELD STAND

GORGIE ROAD
OPEN SEATING

SCHOOL END STAND

MAIN STAND
McLEOD STREET

Travelling Supporters Information:
Routes: From West: Take A71 (Ayr Road) into Gorgie Road, ground is about 0.75 mile past Saughton Park
on left; From North: Take A90 Queensferry Road and turn right into Drum Brae in about 0.5 mile. Follow
Drum Brae into Meadowplace Road (about 1 mile) then Broomhouse Road to junction with Calder Road.
Turn right then as from West; From South: Take A702/A703 to A720 (Oxgangs Road). Turn left and follow
A720 into Wester Hailes Road (2.5 miles) until the junction with Calder Road. Turn right - then as from West.

HIBERNIAN FC

Founded: 1875
Admitted to League: 1893
Former Name(s): None
Nickname: 'The Hi-Bees'
Ground: Easter Road Stadium, Albion Road, Edinburgh   EH7 5QG
Record Attendance: 65,840 (2/1/50)

Colours: Shirts - Green & White
Shorts - White
Telephone No.: (0131) 661-2159
Ticket Information: (0131) 661-1875
Pitch Size: 112 × 74yds
Ground Capacity: 16,200 approx. (all seats)

GENERAL INFORMATION

Supporters Club Administrator: W. Alcorn
Address: 11 Sunnyside, Easter Road Lane, Edinburgh
Telephone Number: (0131) 661-3157
Car Parking: Street Parking
Coach Parking: By Police Direction
Nearest Railway Station: Edinburgh Waverley (25 minutes walk)
Nearest Bus Station: St. Andrew's Square
Club Shop: North Stand
Opening Times: 9.00am - 5.00pm Weekdays
Matchdays 9.00am to kick-off
Telephone No.: (0131) 652-0630
Postal Sales: Yes
Nearest Police Station: Queen Charlotte Street, Leith
Police Force: Lothian & Borders
Police Telephone No.: (0131) 554-9350

GROUND INFORMATION

Away Supporters' Entrances: New South Stand
Away Supporters' Sections: New South Stand

DISABLED INFORMATION

Wheelchairs: 48 spaces available in total in the South Seated Enclosure and the North & South Stands
Disabled Toilets: 2 available in the North and South Stands
The Blind: 10 seats available in the North Stand
Contact Nº: (0131) 661-2159

ADMISSION INFO (1996/97 PRICES)

Adult Seating: £10.00 - £13.00
Child Seating: £5.00
Programme Price: £1.00
FAX Number: (0131) 659-6488

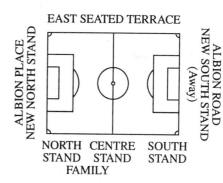

EAST SEATED TERRACE

ALBION PLACE
NEW NORTH STAND

ALBION ROAD
NEW SOUTH STAND
(Away)

NORTH   CENTRE   SOUTH
STAND   STAND   STAND
FAMILY

Travelling Supporters Information:

Routes: From West & North: Take A90 Queensferry Road to A902 and continue for 2.25 miles. Turn right into Great Junction Street and follow into Duke Street then Lochend Road. Turn sharp right into Hawkhill Avenue at Lochend Park and follow road into Albion Place for Ground; From South: Take A1 through Musselburgh (Milton Road/Willow Brae/London Road) and turn right into Easter Road after about 2.5 miles. Take 4th right into Albion Road for Ground.

INVERNESS CALEDONIAN THISTLE FC

Originally Founded: 1885 & 1886
Former Name(s): Caledonian Thistle FC
Nickname: 'The Jags' or 'The Blues'
Ground: The Stadium, East Longman, Inverness
Record Attendance: 9,370 (Telford Street) (1/3/58)
Colours: Shirts - Royal Blue with Red & Black Stripes

Shorts - White
Telephone No.: (01463) 222880 (Ground)
Ticket Information: Contact Secretary
Pitch Size: 115 × 80yds
Ground Capacity: 6,000
Seating Capacity: 2,000 (Approximately)
Contact Address: Mr. J. Falconer, 17 Culloden Park, Inverness
Contact Phone No.: (01463) 792358

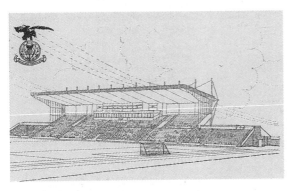

An Artist's impression of the New Ground which will open in November 1996

GENERAL INFORMATION
Supporters Club Administrator: None
Address: c/o Social Club
Telephone Number: (01463) 243526
Car Parking: At Ground
Coach Parking: At Ground
Nearest Railway Station: Inverness (1 mile)
Nearest Bus Station: Inverness
Club Shop: Yes
Opening Times: Matchdays only
Telephone No.: -
Postal Sales: Yes
Nearest Police Station: Raigmore, Inverness
Police Force: Northern Constabulary
Police Telephone No.: (01463) 704006

GROUND INFORMATION
Away Supporters' Entrances: No Segregation
Away Supporters' Sections: No Segregation

DISABLED INFORMATION
Wheelchairs: Accommodation for 16 wheelchairs
Disabled Toilets: Yes
Contact Nº: (01463) 792358 (Bookings necessary)

ADMISSION INFO (1995/96 PRICES)
Adult Standing: £6.00
Adult Seating: £7.00
Child Standing: £3.00
Child Seating: £4.00
Programme Price: £1.00
FAX Number: None

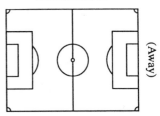

MAIN STAND

(Away)

OPEN TERRACE
(A9 ROAD)

Travelling Supporters Information:
Routes: The Ground is adjacent to Kessock Bridge.   From South: Take the A9 to Inverness and turn right at the roundabout before the bridge over the Moray Firth; From North: Take the A9 over the bridge and turn left at the roundabout for the ground.

KILMARNOCK FC

Founded: 1869
Admitted to League: 1896
Former Name(s): None
Nickname: 'Killie'
Ground: Rugby Park, Rugby Road, Kilmarnock, Ayrshire KA1 2DP
Record Attendance: 34,246 (17/8/63)

Colours: Shirts - Blue & White Stripes
            Shorts - White
Telephone No.: (01563) 525184
Ticket Information: (01563) 542999
Pitch Size: 115 × 72yds
Ground Capacity: 18,128 (all seats)

GENERAL INFORMATION

Supporters Club Administrator: -
Address: c/o Club
Telephone Number: (01563) 528280
Car Parking: Car Park at Ground (Permit Holders only)
Coach Parking: Fairyhill Road Bus Park
Nearest Railway Station: Kilmarnock (15 minutes walk)
Nearest Bus Station: Kilmarnock (10 mins. walk)
Club Shop: 36 Bank Street, Kilmarnock
Opening Times: 9.00am - 5.30pm Monday - Saturday
Telephone No.: (01563) 534210
Postal Sales: Yes
Nearest Police Station: St. Marnock Street, Kilmarnock
Police Force: Strathclyde
Police Telephone No.: (01563) 521188

GROUND INFORMATION

Away Supporters' Entrances: Rugby Road turnstiles
Away Supporters' Sections: Chadwick Stand

DISABLED INFORMATION

Wheelchairs: 15 spaces each for home and away fans in the Main Stand
Disabled Toilets: 2 available in the Chadwick Stand and Moffat Stand
Contact Nº: (01563) 525184 (Bookings necessary)

ADMISSION INFO (1996/97 PRICES)

Adult Seating: £10.00 - £14.00
Child Seating: £4.00 - £5.00
Programme Price: £1.50
FAX Number: (01563) 522181

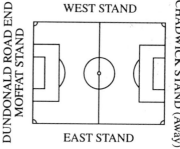

Travelling Supporters Information:
Routes: From Glasgow/Ayr: Take A77 Kilmarnock Bypass. Exit at the Bellfield Interchange. Take A71 (Irvine) to first roundabout then take A759 (Kilmarnock Town Centre). Ground is 0.5 mile on the left hand side.

LIVINGSTON FC

Founded: 1943
Admitted to League: 1974
Former Name(s): Ferranti Thistle FC,
Meadowbank Thistle FC
Nickname: 'Thistle' 'Wee Jags'
Ground: Almondbank Stadium, Alderstone
Road, Livingston
Record Attendance: 4,200 (9/9/74)

Colours: Shirts - Black with Amber Trim
Shorts - Black
Telephone No.: (01506) 417000
Ticket Information: (01506) 417000
Pitch Size: 105 × 72yds
Ground Capacity: 4,000 (all seats)

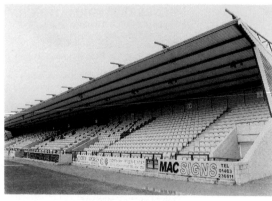

GENERAL INFORMATION
Supporters Club Administrator: None
Address: -
Telephone Number: -
Car Parking: Car Park at Ground
Coach Parking: At Ground
Nearest Railway Station: Livingston
Nearest Bus Station: Livingston
Club Shop: Beneath West Stand
Opening Times: -
Telephone No.: -
Postal Sales: -
Nearest Police Station: Portobello (1 mile)
Police Force: Lothian
Police Telephone No.: (0131) 669-0581

GROUND INFORMATION
Away Supporters' Entrances: East Stand
Away Supporters' Sections: East Stand

DISABLED INFORMATION
Wheelchairs: Accommodated
Disabled Toilets: Yes
Contact Nº: (01506) 417000 (Bookings necessary)

ADMISSION INFO (1996/97 PRICES)
Adult Seating: £7.00
Child Seating: £4.00
1 Adult + 1 Child: £10.00
Programme Price: £1.00
FAX Number: (01875) 811130

EAST STAND
(Away)

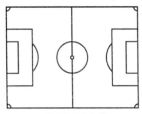

WEST STAND

Travelling Supporters Information:
Routes: Exit M8 at Livingston turn-off and take the A899 to the Cousland Interchange. Turn right into Cousland Road, pass Hospital, then turn left into Alderstone Road and the stadium is on left opposite the Campus.

MONTROSE FC

Founded: 1879
Admitted to League: 1929
Former Name(s): None
Nickname: 'Gable Endies'
Ground: Links Park Stadium, Wellington Street, Montrose   DD10 8QD
Record Attendance: 8,983 (17/3/73)

Colours: Shirts - Royal Blue + White Sleeves
Shorts - White
Telephone No.: (01674) 673200
Ticket Information: (01674) 673200
Pitch Size: 113 × 70yds
Ground Capacity: 4,500
Seating Capacity: 1,338

GENERAL INFORMATION
Supporters Club Administrator:
c/o Links Park
Address: -
Telephone Number: -
Car Parking: Car Park at Ground & Street Parking
Coach Parking: Mid Links
Nearest Railway Station: Montrose Western Road
Nearest Bus Station: High Street, Montrose
Club Shop: At Ground
Opening Times: Fridays & Matchdays 10.00am - 5.00pm
Telephone No.: (01674) 673200
Postal Sales: Yes
Nearest Police Station: Geroge Street, Montrose (15 minutes walk)
Police Force: Tayside
Police Telephone No.: (01674) 672222

GROUND INFORMATION
Away Supporters' Entrances: No Segregation
Away Supporters' Sections: -

DISABLED INFORMATION
Wheelchairs: 5 spaces available in the Main Stand
Disabled Toilets: 2 available in the Main Stand
Contact Nº: (01674) 673200 (Bookings helpful)

ADMISSION INFO (1996/97 PRICES)
Adult Standing: £6.00
Adult Seating: £6.00
Child Standing: £3.00
Child Seating: £3.00
Programme Price: £1.00
FAX Number: (01674) 677311

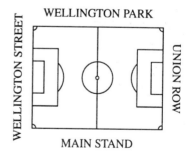

WELLINGTON PARK

WELLINGTON STREET

UNION ROW

MAIN STAND

Travelling Supporters Information:
Routes: Take Main A92 Coastal Road. Once in town, ground is well signposted. Situated in Mid-Links area.

MOTHERWELL FC

Founded: 1886
Admitted to League: 1893
Former Name(s): None
Nickname: 'The Well'
Ground: Fir Park, Fir Park Street, Motherwell ML1 2QN
Record Attendance: 35,632 (12/3/52)

Colours: Shirts - Amber & Claret
Shorts - Claret
Telephone No.: (01698) 333333
Ticket Information: (01698) 333030
Pitch Size: 110 × 75yds
Ground Capacity: 13,742 (all seats)

GENERAL INFORMATION
Supporters Club Administrator: Jim Frame
Address: c/o Fir Park, Motherwell
Telephone Number: -
Car Parking: Street Parking & nearby Car Parks
Coach Parking: Orbiston Street
Nearest Railway Station: Motherwell (1.5 miles)
Nearest Bus Station: Motherwell
Club Shop: At Ground
Opening Times: Weekdays 9.00-4.30pm and Saturday Matchdays 10.00-5.00pm
Telephone No.: (01698) 333333
Postal Sales: Yes
Nearest Police Station: Motherwell (0.25 ml)
Police Force: Strathclyde Region
Police Telephone No.: (01698) 266144

GROUND INFORMATION
Away Supporters' Entrances: Dalziel Drive
Away Supporters' Sections: South Stand

DISABLED INFORMATION
Wheelchairs: 12 spaces for home fans, 6 spaces for away fans accommodated in the South-West Enclosure
Disabled Toilets: One available close to Disabled Area
Contact Nº: (01698) 333333 (Book 1 week before)

ADMISSION INFO (1996/97 PRICES)
Adult Seating: £9.00 - £11.00
Child Seating: £5.00 - £6.00
Programme Price: £1.00
FAX Number: (01698) 276333
Note: Discounts for children in the Family Section

EAST STAND

NORTH STAND

SOUTH STAND (Away)

MAIN STAND
(FIR PARK STREET)

Travelling Supporters Information:
Routes: From East: Take A723 into Merry Street and turn right into Brandon Street (1 mile). Follow through to Windmill Hill Street and turn right at Fire Station into Knowetop Avenue for Ground; From Elsewhere: Exit M74 Junction 4 and take A723 Hamilton Road into Town Centre. Turn right into Brandon Street then as from East.

PARTICK THISTLE FC

Founded: 1876
Admitted to League: 1890
Former Name(s): None
Nickname: 'The Jags'
Ground: Firhill Stadium, 80 Firhill Road, Glasgow G20 7BA
Record Attendance: 49,838 (18/2/22)

Colours: Shirts - Red & Vertical Yellow Stripes
Shorts - Black
Telephone No.: (0141) 945-4811
Ticket Information: (0141) 945-4811
Pitch Size: 110 × 74yds
Ground Capacity: 21,776
Seating Capacity: 9,076

GENERAL INFORMATION
Supporters Club Administrator: Ms. Morag McHaffie
Address: 99 Sommerville Drive, Glasgow
Telephone Number: (0141) 632-3604
Car Parking: Street Parking
Coach Parking: By Police Direction
Nearest Railway Station: Glasgow Queen Street/Glasgow Central/Maryhill
Nearest Underground Station: St. George's Cross/Kelvinbridge
Club Shop: At Ground
Opening Times: Matchdays only 11.30am to 5.00pm or 5.00 to 9.30pm (Night matches)
Telephone No.: (0141) 945-4811
Postal Sales: Yes
Nearest Police Station: Maryhill
Police Force: Strathclyde
Police Telephone No.: (0141) 532-3700

GROUND INFORMATION
Away Supporters' Entrances: Turnstiles 22-39
Away Supporters' Sections: Main Stand 93-172, North Terracing & Jackie Husband Stand 129-231

DISABLED INFORMATION
Wheelchairs: 10 spaces available in North Enclosure
Disabled Toilets: One available in the Main Stand area
The Blind: Facilities may be available on request
Contact Nº: (0141) 945-4811 (Bookings necessary)

ADMISSION INFO (1996/97 PRICES)
Adult Standing: £8.00
Adult Seating: £10.00
Child Standing: £4.00
Child Seating: £5.00
Programme Price: £1.00
FAX Number: (041) 945-1525

JACKIE HUSBAND STAND

NORTH TERRACING

SOUTH TERRACING

(Away) MAIN STAND
FIRHILL ROAD

Travelling Supporters Information:
Routes: From East: Leave M8 at Junction 15; From West: Leave M8 at Junction 17. From both, follow Maryhill Road to Queen's Cross, Ground on right.

QUEEN OF THE SOUTH FC

Founded: 1919
Admitted to League: 1923
Former Name(s): None
Nickname: 'The Doonhamers'
Ground: Palmerston Park, Terregles Street, Dumfries
Record Attendance: 24,500 (23/2/52)

Colours: Shirts - White + Royal Blue Flashes
Shorts - Royal Blue
Telephone No.: (01387) 254853
Ticket Information: (01387) 254853
Pitch Size: 112 × 73yds
Ground Capacity: 8,950 (Approximately)
Seating Capacity: 3,557

GENERAL INFORMATION
Supporters Club Administrator:
J. McCormick
Address: 12 Waverley Road, Dumfries
Telephone Number: (01387) 720938
Car Parking: Car Park adjacent to Ground
Coach Parking: Car Park adjacent to Ground
Nearest Railway Station: Dumfries (0.75 ml)
Nearest Bus Station: Dumfries Whitesands
(5 minutes walk)
Club Shop: Ask at Office
Opening Times: Matchdays Only
Telephone No.: (01384) 254853
Postal Sales: Contact Club
Nearest Police Station: Dumfries (0.5 mile)
Police Force: Dumfries & Galloway
Police Telephone No.: (01387) 252112

GROUND INFORMATION
Away Supporters' Entrances: Terregles Street
Away Supporters' Sections: Terregles Street End

DISABLED INFORMATION
Wheelchairs: Accommodated in front of East Stand
Disabled Toilets: One available in the East Stand
Contact Nº: (01387) 254853

ADMISSION INFO (1996/97 PRICES)
Adult Standing: £6.00
Adult Seating: £8.00
Child Standing: £2.00 - £3.00
Child Seating: £6.00
Programme Price: 80p
FAX Number: (01387) 254853
Note: Special Family Discounts are also available

EAST STAND

PORTLAND ROAD

TERREGLES STREET END
(Away)

WEST STAND
(SOCIAL CLUB)

Travelling Supporters Information:
Routes: From Glasgow: Take M8 to M73 then onto M74 then the A74. Join A701 at Beattock towards Dumfries; From Carlisle: Take A7 then onto the A74 North of Gretna join A75 into Dumfries.

QUEENS PARK FC

Founded: 1867
Admitted to League: 1900
Former Name(s): None
Nickname: 'The Spiders'
Ground: Hampden Park, Mount Florida, Glasgow G42 9BA
Record Attendance: 150,239 (17/4/37)

Colours: Shirts - Black & White Hoops
Shorts - White
Telephone No.: (0141) 632-1275
Ticket Information: (0141) 632-1275
Pitch Size: 115 × 75yds
Ground Capacity: 34,000 (all seats)

GENERAL INFORMATION
Supporters Club Administrator: K.McAllister
Address: 58 Brunton Street, Glasgow G44
Telephone Number: (0141) 637-6075
Car Parking: Car Park at Stadium
Coach Parking: Car Park at Stadium
Nearest Railway Station: Mount Florida and Kings Park (both 5 minutes walk)
Club Shop: Yes
Opening Times: At home matches only
Telephone No.: (0141) 632-1275
Postal Sales: Yes
Nearest Police Station: Aikenhead Road, Glasgow G42
Police Force: Strathclyde
Police Telephone No.: (0141) 422-1113

GROUND INFORMATION
Away Supporters' Entrances: North Stand
Away Supporters' Sections: North Stand – Section D

DISABLED INFORMATION
Limited facilities during rebuilding – contact the club for any Information
Contact Nº: (0141) 632-1275 (Bookings necessary)

ADMISSION INFO (1996/97 PRICES)
Adult Seating: £6.00
Child Seating: £3.00
Programme Price: £1.00
FAX Number: (0141) 636-1612

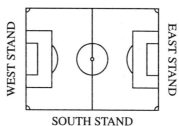

NORTH STAND

WEST STAND

EAST STAND

SOUTH STAND
(BEING REDEVELOPED)

Travelling Supporters Information:
Routes: From the South: Take the A724 to the Cambuslang Road and at Eastfield branch left into Main Street and follow through Burnhill Street and Westmuir Place into Prospecthill Road. Turn left into Aikenhead Road and right into Mount Annan for Kinghorn Drive and the Stadium; From the South: Take the A77 Fenwick Road, through Kilmarnock Road into Pollokshaws Road then turn right into Langside Avenue. Pass through Battle Place to Battlefield Road and turn left into Cathcart Road. Turn right into Letherby Drive, right into Carmunnock Road and 1st left into Mount Annan Drive for the Stadium; From the North & East: Exit M8 Junction 15 and passing Infirmary on left proceed into High Street and cross the Albert Bridge into Crown Street. Join Cathcart Road and proceed South until it becomes Carmunnock Road. Turn left into Mount Annan Drive and left again into Kinghorn Drive for the Stadium.

RAITH ROVERS FC

Founded: 1883
Admitted to League: 1902
Former Name(s): None
Nickname: 'The Rovers'
Ground: Stark's Park, Pratt Street, Kirkcaldy, KY1 1SA
Record Attendance: 31,306 (7/2/53)

Colours: Shirts - Navy with White Trim
Shorts - White with Navy Trim
Telephone No.: (01592) 263514
Ticket Information: (01592) 263514
Pitch Size: 113 × 67yds
Ground Capacity: 10,500 (All Seats)

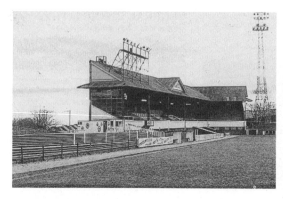

GENERAL INFORMATION
Supporters Club Administrator: F. Hamilton
Address: 22 Tower Terrace, Kirkcaldy
Telephone Number: (01592) 53927
Car Parking: Esplanade and Beveridge Park
Coach Parking: Railway station & Esplanade
Nearest Railway Station: Kirkcaldy (15 mins walk)
Nearest Bus Station: Kirkcaldy (15 minutes walk)
Club Shop: At Ground
Opening Times: 9.00am - 3.00pm Weekdays, 1.30pm - 4.30pm Matchdays
Telephone No.: (01592) 263514
Postal Sales: Yes
Nearest Police Station: Kirkcaldy St. Brycedale Road (15 minutes walk)
Police Force: Fifeshire
Police Telephone No.: (01592) 204444

GROUND INFORMATION
Away Supporters' Entrances: Northgate, Beveridge Park End (Specific games only)
Away Supporters' Sections: North Terracing

DISABLED INFORMATION
Wheelchairs: 10 spaces each for home and away fans accommodated on the North-East trackside
Disabled Toilets: None
Contact Nº: (01592) 263514 (Bookings necessary)

ADMISSION INFO (1996/97 PRICES)
Adult Seating: £12.00
Child Seating: £6.00
Programme Price: £1.00
FAX Number: (01592) 263514
Note: Special Family Discounts are available

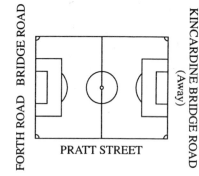

Travelling Supporters Information:
Routes: Take M8 to the end then follow the A90/M90 over the Forth Road Bridge. Exit M90 at junction 1 and follow A921 to Kirkcaldy. On the outskirts of town, turn left at the B & Q roundabout from which the floodlights can be seen. Ground is raised on the hill nearby.

RANGERS FC

photo courtesy of Rangers FC

GENERAL INFORMATION
Supporters Club Administrator:
The Secretary
Address: Rangers Supporters' Association, 250 Edmiston Drive, Glasgow
Telephone Number: (0141) 427-2902
Car Parking: Albion Car Park
Coach Parking: West of Broomloan Stand
Nearest Railway Station: Ibrox (Underground) 2 minutes walk
Nearest Bus Station: Glasgow City Centre
Club Shops: The Rangers Shop, Edmiston House, Glasgow and Copland Road, Glasgow
Opening Times: Monday-Saturday 9.45-5.00
Telephone No.: (0141) 427-3710
Postal Sales: Yes
Nearest Police Station: Orkney Street, Govan
Police Force: Strathclyde Region
Police Telephone No.: (0141) 445-1113

GROUND INFORMATION
Away Supporters' Entrances: Broomloan Road Turnstiles
Away Supporters' Sections: Broomloan Road Stand

DISABLED INFORMATION
Wheelchairs: 60 spaces for home fans, 5 for away fans in front of the West Enclosure
Disabled Toilets: Available in the West Enclosure
The Blind: Commentaries available at the East End of the West Enclosure
Contact N°: (0141) 427-8500 (Bookings necessary)

ADMISSION INFO (1996/97 PRICES)
Adult Seating: £10.00 - £12.00
Child Seating: £7.00
Other Concessions: £9.00
Programme Price: £1.50
FAX Number: (0141) 427-2676

(WEST) GOVAN STAND (EAST)

BROOMLOAN ROAD STAND (Away)

COPLAND ROAD STAND

WEST MAIN STAND EAST
EDMISTON DRIVE

Travelling Supporters Information:
Routes: From All Parts: Exit M8 at Junction 23. Road leads straight to Stadium.

ROSS COUNTY FC

Founded: 1929
Former Name(s): None
Nickname: 'The County'
Ground: Victoria Park, Dingwall, Ross-shire IV15 9QW
Record Attendance: 10,000 vs Rangers (19/2/66)

Colours: Shirts - Navy Blue
Shorts - White
Telephone No.: (01349) 862253
Pitch Size: 110 × 72yds
Ground Capacity: 6,500
Seating Capacity: 1,519
Contact Address: The Secretary, c/o Ground
Contact Phone No.: (01349) 862253

GENERAL INFORMATION
Supporters Club Administrator: B.Campbell
Address: c/o Ross County FC, Victoria Park, Dingwall
Telephone Number: (01349) 862253
Car Parking: At Ground
Coach Parking: At Ground
Nearest Railway Station: Dingwall (Adjacent)
Nearest Bus Station: Dingwall
Club Shop: Yes
Opening Times: Weekdays & Matchdays
Telephone No.: (01349) 862253
Postal Sales: Yes
Nearest Police Station: Dingwall
Police Force: Northern Constabulary
Police Telephone No.: (01349) 862444

GROUND INFORMATION
Away Supporters' Entrances: East Stand
Away Supporters' Sections: East Stand

DISABLED INFORMATION
Wheelchairs: 6 spaces each for home and away fans
Disabled Toilets: Available at the bottom of the West Stand
Contact Nº: (01349) 862253 (Bookings necessary)

ADMISSION INFO (1996/97 PRICES)
Adult Standing: £6.00
Adult Seating: £7.00
Child Standing: £3.00
Child Seating: £4.00
Programme Price: £1.00
FAX Number: (01349) 862277

WEST
STAND

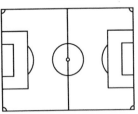

MAIN STAND

Travelling Supporters Information:
Routes: Ground is situated at Dingwall adjacent to the Railway Station, down Jubilee Park Road at the bottom of the High Street.

ST. JOHNSTONE FC

Founded: 1884
Admitted to League: 1911
Former Name(s): None
Nickname: 'Saints'
Ground: McDiarmid Park, Crieff Road, Perth PH1 2SJ
Record Attendance: 10,504 (30/10/90)

Colours: Shirts - Blue
Shorts - White
Telephone No.: (01738) 626961
Ticket Information: (01738) 626961
Pitch Size: 115 × 75yds
Ground Capacity: 10,721 (all seats)

GENERAL INFORMATION
Supporters Club Administrator: J. McLeish
Address: 157 Dunkeld Road, Perth PH1 3AE
Telephone Number: (01738) 442022
Car Parking: Car Park at Ground
Coach Parking: At Ground
Nearest Railway Station: Perth (3 miles)
Nearest Bus Station: Perth (3 miles)
Club Shop: At Ground
Opening Times: 9.00am - 5.00pm
Telephone No.: (01738) 626961
Postal Sales: Yes
Nearest Police Station: Perth (1.5 miles)
Police Force: Tayside
Police Telephone No.: (01738) 621141

GROUND INFORMATION
Away Supporters' Entrances: North Stand Side
Away Supporters' Sections: North Stand & North End of West Stand

DISABLED INFORMATION
Wheelchairs: 15 spaces each for home and away fans in the East and West Stands
Disabled Toilets: 2 in both the East and West Stands
The Blind: 24 headphones around the stadium to listen to live broadcast
Contact Nº: (01738) 626961 (Booking necessary)

ADMISSION INFO (1996/97 PRICES)
Adult Seating: £6.00 - £11.00
Child Seating: £4.00 - £7.00
Programme Price: £1.00
FAX Number: (01738) 625771
Note: Reduced rates available in Family Stand

WEST STAND
(MAIN STAND)

ORMOND STAND
(FAMILY STAND)

NORTH STAND
(Away)

EAST STAND

Travelling Supporters Information:
Routes: Follow M80 to Stirling, take A9 Inverness Road north from Perth and follow signs to 'Football Stadium'. Ground is beside dual-carriageway - Perth Western By-Pass near junction 11 on the M90.

ST. MIRREN FC

Founded: 1877
Admitted to League: 1890 (Founder Member)
Former Name(s): None
Nickname: 'The Saints' 'The Buddies'
Ground: St. Mirren Park, Love Street, Paisley PA3 2EJ
Record Attendance: 47,428 (7/3/25)

Colours: Shirts - Black & White Stripes
Shorts - White
Telephone No.: (0141) 889-2558
Ticket Information: (0141) 889-2558
Pitch Size: 110 × 70yds
Ground Capacity: 15,410
Seating Capacity: 9,395

GENERAL INFORMATION

Supporters Club Administrator: Ian Cuthbertson
Address: Knox Street, Paisley
Telephone Number: (0141) 887-2101
Car Parking: Street Parking
Coach Parking: Racecourse - Paisley
Nearest Railway Station: Paisley Gilmour Street (400 yards)
Nearest Bus Station: Paisley
Club Shop: At Stadium
Opening Times: Matchdays only 9.30-2.00
Telephone No.: (0141) 840-1337
Postal Sales: Yes
Nearest Police Station: Mill Street, Paisley (1 mile)
Police Force: 'K' Division, Strathclyde
Police Telephone No.: (0141) 889-1113

GROUND INFORMATION

Away Supporters' Entrances: West of Main Stand
Away Supporters' Sections: North Bank - West Stand

DISABLED INFORMATION

Wheelchairs: Accommodated in the West Stand
Disabled Toilets: 2 available in the West Stand
Contact Nº: (0141) 840-1337 (Booking necessary)

ADMISSION INFO (1996/97 PRICES)

Adult Standing: £8.00
Adult Seating: £9.00 - £10.00
Child Standing: £4.00
Child Seating: £4.50 - £5.00
Programme Price: £1.00
FAX Number: (0141) 848-6444

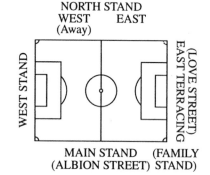

NORTH STAND
WEST   EAST
(Away)

WEST STAND

(LOVE STREET)
EAST TERRACING

MAIN STAND   (FAMILY
(ALBION STREET) STAND)

Travelling Supporters Information:
Routes: From All Parts: Exit M8 Junction 29 and take A760 Paisley Road. Ground approx. 0.5 miles along on the left - floodlights clearly visible for some distance.

STENHOUSEMUIR FC

Founded: 1884	**Colours**: Shirts - Maroon
Admitted to League: 1921	Shorts - White
Former Name(s): None	**Telephone No.**: (01324) 562992
Nickname: 'Warriors'	**Ticket Information**: (01324) 562992
Ground: Ochilview Park, Gladstone Road,	**Pitch Size**: 110 × 72yds
Stenhousemuir FK5 5QL	**Ground Capacity**: 3,500
Record Attendance: 12,500 (11/3/50)	**Seating Capacity**: 1,040

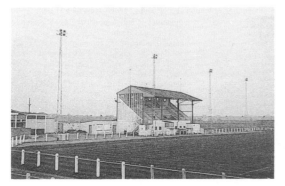

GENERAL INFORMATION
Supporters Club Administrator:
K. Baird
Address: c/o Club
Telephone Number: (01324) 562992
Car Parking: Large Car Park Adjacent
Coach Parking: Behind Grandstand
Nearest Railway Station: Larbert (1 mile)
Nearest Bus Station: Falkirk (2.5 miles)
Club Shop: At Ground
Opening Times: Monday – Friday 9.00am to
4.00pm + 1 hour before & after home games
Telephone No.: (01324) 562992
Postal Sales: Yes
Nearest Police Station: Stenhousemuir (0.5 mile)
Police Force: Central Scotland
Police Telephone No.: (01324) 562112

GROUND INFORMATION
Away Supporters' Entrances: Main Stand
Away Supporters' Sections: Main Stand

DISABLED INFORMATION
Wheelchairs: Accommodation not specified
Disabled Toilets: Available in the new Gladstone Road Stand
Contact Nº: (01324) 562992

ADMISSION INFO (1996/97 PRICES)
Adult Standing: £7.00
Adult Seating: £8.00
Child Standing: £4.00
Child Seating: £5.00
Programme Price: £1.00
FAX Number: (01324) 562992

MAIN STAND
(Away)

TRYST ROAD

NEW STAND
GLADSTONE ROAD

Travelling Supporters Information:
Routes: Exit M876 at Junction 2 and follow signs for Stenhousemuir. Pass the Old Hospital and turn right after the Golf Course. Ground is on the left behind houses - floodlights visible for 0.25 mile.

STIRLING ALBION FC

Founded: 1945
Admitted to League: 1946
Former Name(s): None
Nickname: 'The Albion'
Ground: Forth Bank Stadium, Spring Kerse, Stirling   FK7 7UJ
Record Attendance: 3,808 vs Aberdeen
(17/2/96)

Colours: Shirts - Red with White Sleeves
Shorts - White
Telephone No.: (01786) 450399
Pitch Size: 113 × 78yds
Ground Capacity: 3,808
Seating Capacity: 2,500

GENERAL INFORMATION
Supporters Club Administrator: S.Torrance
Address: c/o Club
Telephone Number: -
Car Parking: Large Car Park Adjacent
Coach Parking: Adjacent to Ground
Nearest Railway Station: Stirling (2 miles)
Nearest Bus Station: Stirling (2 miles)
Club Shop: Yes
Opening Times: Matchdays Only
Telephone No.: (01786) 450399
Postal Sales: Yes
Nearest Police Station: Stirling (2 miles)
Police Force: Central Scotland
Police Telephone No.: (01786) 456000

GROUND INFORMATION
Away Supporters' Entrances: South Terracing
Away Supporters' Sections: South Terracing & East Stand

DISABLED INFORMATION
Wheelchairs: 18 spaces each for home and away fans
Disabled Toilets: 2 available beneath each stand
Contact Nº: (01786) 450399

ADMISSION INFO (1996/97 PRICES)
Adult Standing: £8.00
Adult Seating: £9.00
Child Standing: £4.00
Child Seating: £5.00
Programme Price: £1.00
FAX Number: (01786) 448592

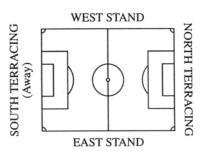

Travelling Supporters Information:
Routes: Take Stirling signs from M9/M80 Northbound. From Pirnhall Roundabout follow signs for Alloa/ St. Andrew's to 4th roundabout and then turn left for stadium.

STRANRAER FC

Founded: 1870	**Colours**: Shirts - Blue
Admitted to League: 1955	Shorts - White with Blue Wedge
Former Name(s): None	**Telephone No.**: (01776) 703271
Nickname: 'The Blues'	**Ticket Information**: (01776) 703271
Ground: Stair Park, London Road, Stranraer,	**Pitch Size**: 110 × 70yds
DG9 8BS	**Ground Capacity**: 5,000
Record Attendance: 6,500 (24/1/48)	**Seating Capacity**: 1,900

GENERAL INFORMATION
Supporters Club Administrator:
Miss Margaret Rennie
Address: c/o Club
Telephone Number: -
Car Parking: Car Park at Ground
Coach Parking: Port Rodie, Stranraer
Nearest Railway Station: Stranraer (1 mile)
Nearest Bus Station: Port Rodie, Stranraer
Club Shop: At Ground
Opening Times: 2.30-3.00pm & Half-time
Telephone No.: -
Postal Sales: Write to 28 Springfield Crescent
Stranraer
Nearest Police Station: Stranraer (0.75 mile)
Police Force: Dumfries & Galloway
Police Telephone No.: (01776) 702112

GROUND INFORMATION
Away Supporters' Entrances: Opposite South Stand
Away Supporters' Sections: Visitors Stand
DISABLED INFORMATION
Wheelchairs: 6 spaces each for home and away fans in front of the North Stand
Disabled Toilets: One available in the North Stand
Contact Nº: (01776) 702194
ADMISSION INFO (1996/97 PRICES)
Adult Standing: £6.00
Adult Seating: £7.50
Child Standing: £3.00
Child Seating: £4.50
Programme Price: £1.00
FAX Number: (01776) 702194

LONDON ROAD (A74)
VISITORS STAND

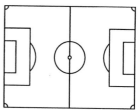

SOUTH STAND

Travelling Supporters Information:
Routes: From West: Take A75 to Stranraer, ground is on the left-hand side of the road in a public park shortly after entering the town; From North: Take A77 and follow to join with A75 (then as West). Ground is set back from the road and floodlights are visible.

STATISTICS

SEASON 1995-96

Contents:

Premier Division
Home & Away Chart
Final Table

1st Division
Home & Away Chart
Final Table

2nd Division
Home & Away Chart
Final Table

3rd Division
Home & Away Chart

Highland League
Home & Away Chart + Final Table
Final Table

East of Scotland League
Premier League & 1st Division :
Home & Away Charts + Final Tables

Scottish League Premier Division Season 1995/96	Aberdeen	Celtic	Falkirk	Heart of Midlothian	Hibernian	Kilmarnock	Motherwell	Partick Thistle	Raith Rovers	Rangers
Aberdeen	■	2-3	3-1	1-2	1-2	4-1	1-0	3-0	3-0	0-1
	■	1-2	2-1	1-1	2-1	3-0	2-1	1-0	1-0	0-1
Celtic	2-0	■	1-0	3-1	2-2	4-2	1-1	2-1	0-0	0-2
	5-0	■	4-0	4-0	2-1	1-1	1-0	4-0	4-1	0-0
Falkirk	2-3	0-1	■	2-0	2-0	0-2	0-0	0-1	2-1	0-2
	1-1	0-0	■	0-2	1-1	4-2	4-0	1-2	2-3	0-4
Heart of Midlothian	1-2	0-4	4-1	■	2-1	2-1	1-1	3-0	4-2	0-2
	1-3	1-2	2-1	■	1-1	1-0	4-0	2-5	2-0	2-0
Hibernian	1-1	0-4	2-1	2-2	■	2-0	4-2	3-0	1-2	1-4
	1-2	1-2	2-1	2-1	■	1-1	0-0	1-0	1-1	0-2
Kilmarnock	1-2	0-0	4-0	3-1	0-3	■	1-1	2-1	5-1	0-2
	1-1	0-0	1-0	0-2	3-2	■	0-1	2-1	2-0	0-3
Motherwell	2-1	0-2	1-1	0-0	0-2	3-0	■	1-1	0-2	0-0
	1-0	0-0	1-0	1-1	3-0	0-1	■	0-2	1-0	1-3
Partick Thistle	1-0	1-2	1-1	2-0	1-1	1-1	1-0	■	0-2	0-4
	1-1	2-4	0-3	0-1	0-0	0-1	0-2	■	0-3	1-2
Raith Rovers	1-0	0-1	0-1	1-1	3-0	2-0	0-0	3-1	■	2-2
	2-2	1-3	1-0	1-3	1-0	1-1	2-0	0-2	■	2-4
Rangers	1-1	3-3	2-0	4-1	0-1	1-0	2-1	1-0	4-0	■
	3-1	1-1	3-2	0-3	7-0	3-0	3-2	5-0	4-0	■

SCOTLAND PREMIER DIVISION 1995/96

LEAGUE TABLE FINAL

Rangers	36	27	6	3	85	25	87
Celtic	36	24	11	1	74	25	83
Aberdeen	36	16	7	13	52	45	55
Heart of Midlothian	36	16	7	13	55	53	55
Hibernian	36	11	10	15	43	57	43
Raith Rovers	36	12	7	17	41	57	43
Kilmarnock	36	11	8	17	39	54	41
Motherwell	36	9	12	15	28	39	39
Partick Thistle	36	8	6	22	29	62	30
Falkirk	36	6	6	24	31	60	24

Champions : - Rangers

Relegated : - Falkirk and Partick Thistle

In the Premier Division/First Division Play-Off matches, Dundee United defeated Partick Thistle by three goals to two on aggregate. Therefore, Dundee United have been promoted to the Premier Division and Partick Thistle have been relegated to the First Division

Scottish League Division One Season 1995/96	Airdrieonians	Clydebank	Dumbarton	Dundee	Dundee United	Dunfermline Athletic	Hamilton Academ.	Greenock Morton	St. Johnstone	St. Mirren
Airdrieonians	■	1-1	2-1	2-3	1-1	0-1	0-0	3-2	1-1	1-2
	■	1-1	5-1	0-0	1-1	1-2	3-0	0-2	1-3	1-3
Clydebank	1-1	■	2-1	1-1	1-2	0-4	2-0	1-0	2-0	1-1
	2-1	■	1-0	0-1	1-1	2-3	1-3	0-1	1-2	1-2
Dumbarton	1-2	1-2	■	1-5	1-0	0-4	1-0	0-2	1-3	0-0
	1-2	0-1	■	1-2	1-3	0-3	1-2	0-1	0-3	0-1
Dundee	1-1	1-1	1-1	■	2-3	2-4	1-1	0-0	0-1	3-1
	2-0	3-0	3-0	■	0-2	1-1	2-1	1-1	0-0	1-2
Dundee United	1-2	3-0	8-0	2-3	■	3-1	2-1	1-1	2-1	1-0
	2-2	6-0	6-1	2-0	■	0-1	1-1	4-0	1-3	2-1
Dunfermline Athletic	2-0	2-1	3-1	0-1	3-0	■	4-0	0-2	2-1	1-1
	2-1	4-3	4-1	1-1	2-2	■	1-3	4-1	3-2	2-2
Hamilton Academicals	1-2	0-2	3-0	1-2	0-1	1-3	■	2-3	0-3	2-2
	4-1	1-1	2-1	0-1	0-2	0-0	■	0-1	2-1	3-0
Greenock Morton	2-1	3-0	1-2	2-2	2-0	2-0	2-0	■	4-0	0-3
	3-0	0-0	2-0	1-0	1-2	1-1	4-1	■	1-0	1-2
St. Johnstone	1-0	2-2	4-1	0-2	0-0	1-0	2-0	0-2	■	0-0
	0-0	3-1	3-0	3-2	1-0	2-2	4-1	6-1	■	1-0
St. Mirren	1-2	2-1	3-2	1-2	1-1	0-2	0-3	1-4	0-0	■
	2-1	1-2	5-0	2-1	1-3	2-1	0-1	0-1	1-3	■

SCOTLAND 1ST DIVISION 1995/96

LEAGUE TABLE FINAL

Dunfermline Athletic	36	21	8	7	73	41	71
Dundee United	36	19	10	7	73	37	67
Greenock Morton	36	20	7	9	57	39	67
St. Johnstone	36	19	8	9	60	36	65
Dundee	36	15	12	9	53	40	57
St. Mirren	36	13	8	15	46	51	47
Clydebank	36	10	10	16	39	58	40
Airdrieonians	36	9	11	16	43	54	38
Hamilton Academical	36	10	6	20	40	57	36
Dumbarton	36	3	2	31	23	94	11

Promoted : - Dunfermline Athletic and Dundee United
Relegated : - Hamilton Academical and Dumbarton

Scottish League Division Two Season 1995/96	Ayr United	Berwick Rangers	Clyde	East Fife	Forfar Athletic	Montrose	Queen Of The South	Stenhousemuir	Stirling Albion	Stranraer
Ayr United		1-4	1-1	0-1	1-3	2-0	2-0	1-2	1-2	0-0
		5-0	2-1	1-0	2-1	2-0	3-0	1-1	2-2	0-0
Berwick Rangers	2-2		0-0	0-1	1-0	2-2	0-0	3-1	3-0	4-0
	2-1		2-3	1-2	1-0	4-1	4-1	2-1	0-3	1-0
Clyde	1-2	3-1		0-1	1-2	3-0	2-1	0-1	1-2	1-1
	2-0	2-1		2-2	3-1	1-3	0-0	3-0	1-3	2-2
East Fife	1-0	1-0	0-0		1-1	3-0	2-1	0-2	0-3	3-3
	1-1	0-0	1-1		1-0	7-0	1-1	3-1	0-1	2-1
Forfar Athletic	2-1	1-4	1-0	0-2		0-0	2-1	1-0	0-6	0-0
	1-0	1-3	4-2	0-2		2-1	0-3	3-1	1-4	2-2
Montrose	0-1	1-3	2-3	1-2	1-0		1-4	1-4	2-2	0-0
	0-1	1-2	0-0	0-1	3-1		0-6	1-3	0-3	4-2
Queen Of The South	0-0	1-4	0-3	0-2	1-1	4-2		2-2	1-5	0-3
	2-2	3-0	2-1	1-0	4-1	1-1		3-3	0-7	2-1
Stenhousemuir	1-1	4-1	0-1	0-1	3-1	3-1	2-1		1-1	3-0
	0-1	0-3	1-0	2-2	0-2	3-1	1-3		0-1	2-0
Stirling Albion	2-0	1-0	1-1	0-2	4-1	3-0	2-2	2-1		1-1
	2-0	4-3	3-0	2-2	1-0	2-0	4-1	0-1		2-0
Stranraer	2-0	0-0	0-0	2-0	1-1	4-1	0-0	2-1	0-0	
	1-1	0-3	2-2	0-0	1-0	1-2	3-1	0-0	2-2	

SCOTLAND 2ND DIVISION 1995/96

LEAGUE TABLE FINAL

Stirling Albion	36	24	9	3	83	30	81
East Fife	36	19	10	7	50	29	67
Berwick Rangers	36	18	6	12	64	47	60
Stenhousemuir	36	14	7	15	51	49	49
Clyde	36	11	12	13	47	45	45
Ayr United	36	11	12	13	40	40	45
Queen of South	36	11	10	15	54	67	43
Stranraer	36	8	18	10	38	43	42
Forfar Athletic	36	11	7	18	37	61	40
Montrose	36	5	5	26	33	86	20

Promoted : - Stirling Albion and East Fife
Relegated : - Forfar Athletic and Montrose

Scottish League Division Three Season 1995/96	Albion Rovers	Alloa Athletic	Arbroath	Brechin City	Caledonian Thistle	Cowdenbeath	East Stirlingshire	Livingston	Queen's Park	Ross County
Albion Rovers		2-1	0-2	1-0	2-2	2-3	1-2	0-2	3-1	3-4
		1-0	1-1	0-0	0-2	2-0	2-2	0-1	0-2	0-3
Alloa Athletic	3-2		0-2	3-2	0-5	2-3	1-3	0-2	0-0	1-0
	3-1		0-3	0-3	0-2	2-1	2-2	1-1	0-1	0-4
Arbroath	2-0	1-1		1-1	2-1	2-1	2-2	1-3	1-1	1-2
	2-1	1-0		0-1	1-2	0-0	2-1	1-2	1-1	1-1
Brechin City	0-1	0-1	1-1		0-0	2-0	3-1	2-0	1-0	2-1
	1-0	3-0	0-1		0-1	2-0	4-1	0-1	4-0	0-0
Caledonian Thistle	6-1	1-1	5-1	1-2		3-2	1-1	0-3	3-1	1-1
	1-1	0-0	1-1	0-1		2-0	0-3	1-2	1-1	1-1
Cowdenbeath	4-1	1-0	1-1	0-1	0-0		4-2	0-1	3-2	2-0
	1-1	3-0	1-2	0-0	2-1		1-4	0-3	2-3	1-1
East Stirlingshire	5-1	2-2	0-1	2-0	0-5	3-1		1-2	1-2	1-2
	1-1	1-0	1-0	3-0	1-5	1-1		0-3	1-2	2-4
Livingston	2-1	2-0	0-1	0-0	0-2	0-1	1-1		2-0	0-0
	0-1	1-0	3-0	0-1	2-2	2-1	1-1		3-1	2-1
Queen's Park	4-1	0-0	2-0	0-2	0-3	3-1	1-0	0-1		1-1
	5-1	0-0	0-0	0-0	1-2	2-1	2-2	0-0		0-0
Ross County	5-1	2-2	4-2	0-0	2-0	2-2	1-1	1-1	2-0	
	1-1	0-0	0-0	1-2	2-1	4-1	2-2	1-3	0-1	

SCOTLAND 3RD DIVISION 1995/96

LEAGUE TABLE FINAL

Livingston	36	21	9	6	51	24	72
Brechin City	36	18	9	9	41	21	63
Caledonian Thistle	36	15	12	9	64	38	57
Ross County	36	12	17	7	56	39	53
Arbroath	36	13	13	10	41	41	52
Queen's Park	36	12	12	12	40	43	48
East Stirlingshire	36	11	11	14	58	62	44
Cowdenbeath	36	10	8	18	45	59	38
Alloa Athletic	36	6	11	19	26	58	29
Albion Rovers	36	7	8	21	37	74	29

Promoted : - Livingston and Brechin City

	Brora Rangers	Buckie Thistle	Clachnacuddin	Cove Rangers	Deveronvale	Elgin City	Forres Mechanics	Fort William	Fraserburgh	Huntly	Keith	Lossiemouth	Nairn County	Peterhead	Rothes	Wick Academy
Brora Rangers		0-0	0-3	1-3	2-1	0-0	0-0	3-1	0-5	1-2	1-0	1-2	3-2	3-2	1-1	0-2
Buckie Thistle	1-1		0-1	1-5	0-1	4-1	1-0	4-0	1-1	0-3	2-2	0-4	0-3	0-4	2-2	5-2
Clachnacuddin	4-3	2-1		1-2	0-0	3-4	2-0	5-2	2-2	1-2	1-1	0-1	1-1	1-2	1-1	2-2
Cove Rangers	2-1	3-0	2-1		4-0	2-1	3-1	4-1	2-4	3-1	4-5	0-0	4-1	2-2	1-2	2-1
Deveronvale	0-2	2-1	2-1	1-5		2-4	1-1	4-1	1-5	2-1	0-1	0-1	4-0	2-4	2-0	0-1
Elgin City	0-1	1-4	3-2	0-0	3-0		0-2	3-1	2-6	1-2	3-2	3-0	5-0	1-3	4-3	4-0
Forres Mechs.	3-0	1-1	0-2	1-2	1-4	1-2		2-0	1-1	1-3	1-2	2-3	0-0	3-5	1-2	4-0
Fort William	0-4	2-1	0-1	0-1	1-2	3-0	0-0		1-4	0-3	0-2	0-2	2-1	1-0	3-1	1-2
Fraserburgh	2-0	7-2	7-0	1-1	0-1	1-1	1-1	5-0		1-3	4-6	5-2	2-2	4-0	1-1	4-0
Huntly	4-1	3-0	4-2	1-0	1-0	3-1	3-0	8-1	7-4		2-0	5-1	4-0	3-6	6-2	7-0
Keith	5-1	0-3	0-0	2-3	0-0	0-2	5-0	4-0	4-2	1-2		4-1	2-0	4-0	1-1	2-1
Lossiemouth	3-0	1-0	1-0	2-2	5-0	3-0	2-1	0-1	0-1	0-3	1-0		5-0	2-1	4-0	1-2
Nairn County	1-3	1-1	2-1	0-3	1-10	0-4	1-5	2-3	0-3	0-2	1-0	1-2		1-4	3-2	0-4
Peterhead	1-2	1-1	2-1	2-1	3-1	4-1	5-2	1-1	1-1	3-6	2-2	4-0	2-0		4-2	2-2
Rothes	0-3	5-6	0-3	0-3	2-3	3-4	0-3	2-0	3-1	0-5	0-1	0-0	1-1	0-3		2-2
Wick Academy	0-2	2-3	4-1	1-5	2-1	0-1	0-0	0-1	1-0	2-4	2-1	1-5	3-1	1-1	2-1	

HIGHLAND LEAGUE 1995/96

LEAGUE TABLE FINAL

Huntly	30	27	0	3	103	37	81
Cove Rangers	30	20	5	5	74	35	65
Lossiemouth	30	18	3	9	54	37	57
Peterhead	30	16	7	7	74	51	55
Fraserburgh	30	14	9	7	85	46	51
Keith	30	14	6	10	59	40	48
Elgin City	30	15	3	12	59	55	48
Brora Rangers	30	12	5	13	40	50	41
Deveronvale	30	12	3	15	47	53	39
Wick Academy	30	11	5	14	42	63	38
Clachnacuddin	30	9	7	14	45	51	34
Buckie Thistle	30	8	8	14	45	61	32
Forres Mechs.	30	6	8	16	38	51	26
Fort William	30	8	2	20	27	71	26
Rothes	30	4	8	18	39	74	20
Nairn County	30	4	5	21	26	85	17

East of Scotland Premier Division Season 1995/96	Annan Athletic	Civil Service Strollers	Craigroyston	Edinburgh Univ.	Gala Fairydean	Pencaitland	Preston Athletic	Spartans	Vale of Leithen	Whitehill Welfare
Annan Athletic		4-0	2-2	1-1	2-3	1-0	6-1	1-2	2-1	3-2
Civil Service Str.	2-3		1-4	1-0	0-2	2-3	2-2	3-0	2-2	0-3
Craigroyston	1-1	1-4		2-2	1-1	2-2	2-2	3-1	2-0	1-4
Edinburgh Univ.	2-4	2-0	1-4		1-1	0-0	2-2	1-3	1-0	0-1
Gala Fairydean	2-2	1-0	4-1	2-1		2-2	0-1	3-0	4-5	2-0
Pencaitland	0-2	2-2	2-1	2-0	4-1		1-1	1-2	1-1	1-5
Preston Athletic	2-2	2-0	1-4	1-1	0-2	2-1		2-3	4-1	1-4
Spartans	3-0	1-1	0-1	3-1	0-2	0-2	2-1		0-0	0-1
Vale of Leithen	3-3	2-2	3-1	1-3	2-3	2-1	2-2	3-4		0-10
Whitehill Welfare	4-1	6-2	5-0	3-0	3-1	2-0	7-2	4-1	5-0	

East of Scotland First Division Season 1995/96	Coldstream	Easthouses Lily	Edinburgh City	Eyemouth United	Hawick Royal A.	Heriot-Watt Univ.	Kelso United	Lothian Thistle	Manor Thistle	Peebles Rovers	Selkirk	Tollcross United
Coldstream		3-0	2-3	0-0	3-3	1-4	0-2	4-1	0-2	0-5	3-5	0-4
Easthouses Lily	2-2		3-3	4-0	6-1	4-1	1-0	0-3	3-2	1-3	4-3	2-3
Edinburgh City	2-0	7-1		8-0	4-0	4-2	3-0	2-3	1-2	2-2	1-0	3-2
Eyemouth United	0-0	0-6	2-4		3-2	3-1	2-3	2-3	6-2	1-2	3-0	3-4
Hawick Royal A.	3-1	1-7	3-3	2-2		5-0	1-2	2-0	1-4	3-4	1-0	3-1
Heriot-Watt Univ.	2-2	1-3	1-5	1-3	2-1		1-2	1-2	0-3	1-0	3-5	2-6
Kelso United	1-4	2-4	2-4	2-1	1-1	5-1		1-0	1-3	1-2	2-5	3-3
Lothian Thistle	5-3	4-2	0-2	4-0	4-1	2-1	3-0		2-2	1-2	1-2	0-2
Manor Thistle	0-0	7-1	3-3	3-0	2-1	3-1	3-0	2-2		4-0	5-1	3-0
Peebles Rovers	1-1	4-1	3-0	1-3	0-6	1-3	4-1	1-2	3-0		1-2	3-1
Selkirk	1-1	1-1	1-2	1-5	1-1	4-2	3-2	2-2	0-2	1-0		0-0
Tollcross United	1-0	0-2	0-1	1-1	0-3	2-2	4-1	1-3	3-1	4-3	1-3	

EAST OF SCOTLAND LEAGUE
PREMIER DIVISION 1995/96

LEAGUE TABLE FINAL

Whitehill Welfare	18	16	0	2	71	14	48
Gala Fairydean	18	10	4	4	37	25	34
Annan Athletic	18	9	6	3	41	30	33
Spartans	18	8	2	8	24	32	26
Craigroyston	18	6	4	8	33	37	22
Pencaitland	18	5	6	7	25	28	21
Preston Athletic	18	4	7	7	29	42	19
Edinburgh University	18	3	6	9	18	31	15
Vale of Leithen	18	3	6	9	28	50	15
Civil Service Strollers	18	3	5	10	24	41	14

Relegated : - Vale of Leithen and Civil Service Strollers

EAST OF SCOTLAND LEAGUE
FIRST DIVISION 1995/96

LEAGUE TABLE FINAL

Edinburgh City	22	14	5	3	67	33	47
Manor Thistle	22	14	4	4	58	29	46
Lothian Thistle	22	12	3	7	46	34	39
Peebles Rovers	22	11	3	8	46	38	36
Easthouses Lily	22	11	3	8	58	51	36
Selkirk	22	18	4	8	44	42	34
Tollcross United	22	9	4	9	41	40	31
Eyemouth United	22	8	3	11	40	55	27
Hawick Royal Albert	22	7	5	10	45	50	26
Kelso	22	7	2	13	31	50	23
Coldstream	22	3	8	11	30	47	17
Heriot-Watt University	22	3	2	17	32	69	11

Promoted : - Edinburgh City and Manor Thistle

HIGHLAND FOOTBALL LEAGUE

Founded
1893

Secretary
Mr. J. H. Grant

Address
35 Hamilton Drive,
ELGIN   IV30 2NN

Phone
(01343) 544995

BRORA RANGERS FC

Founded: 1878/79
Former Name(s): None
Nickname: 'The Cattachs'
Ground: Dudgeon Park, Brora
Record Attendance: 2,000 (1963/64)
Colours: Shirts - Red
         Shorts - White
Telephone No.: (01408) 621570

Ticket Information: (01408) 621231
Pitch Size: 112 × 70yds
Ground Capacity: 4,000
Seating Capacity: 250
Contact Address: James Fraser, Craiglyn,
Victoria Road, Brora   KW9 6QN
Contact Phone No.: (01408) 621231

GENERAL INFORMATION
Supporters Club Administrator: Secretary
Address: c/o Club
Telephone Number: (01408) 621570
Car Parking: Adjacent to Ground
Coach Parking: Adjacent to Ground
Nearest Railway Station: Brora
Nearest Bus Station: Brora
Club Shop: At Ground
Opening Times: Matchdays Only
Telephone No.: (01408) 621231
Postal Sales: Yes
Nearest Police Station: Brora
Police Force: Northern Constabulary
Police Telephone No.: (01408) 621222

GROUND INFORMATION
Away Supporters' Entrances: No Segregation
Away Supporters' Sections: No Segregation
ADMISSION INFO (1996/97 PRICES)
Adult Standing: £3.00
Adult Seating: £3.50
Child Standing: £1.50
Child Seating: £2.00
Programme Price: 50p
FAX Number: None

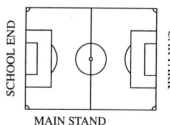

SEAFORTH ENCLOSURE

SCHOOL END

SOCIAL CLUB CAR PARK

MAIN STAND

Travelling Supporters Information:
Routes: Take A9 Northbound from Inverness and the Stadium is on the right upon entering the town - clearly visible from the road.

BUCKIE THISTLE FC

Founded: 1889	**Telephone No.**: (01542) 836468
Former Name(s): None	**Pitch Size**: 109 × 73yds
Nickname: 'The Jags'	**Ground Capacity**: 5,400
Ground: Victoria Park, Mid Mar Street,	**Seating Capacity**: 400
Buckie, Banffshire	**Contact Address**: George Jappy (Secretary),
Record Attendance: 8,600 vs Falkirk (1/3/58)	Ashness, 11 Stuart Street, Portessie, Buckie
Colours: Shirts - Green & White Hoops	**Contact Phone No.**: (01542) 831506 / (01343)
Shorts - White	528000

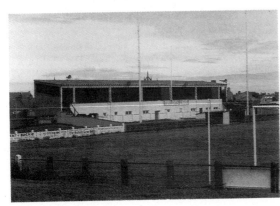

GENERAL INFORMATION
Supporters Club Administrator: -
Address: -
Telephone Number: -
Car Parking: Adjacent to Ground
Coach Parking: Adjacent to Ground
Nearest Railway Station: Keith (12 miles)
Nearest Bus Station: Buckie
Club Shop: None
Opening Times: -
Telephone No.: -
Postal Sales: -
Nearest Police Station: Buckie
Police Force: Grampian Police
Police Telephone No.: (01542) 832222
Social Club: Buckie Thistle Social Club, 3/5
West Church Street, Buckie
Telephone No.: (01542) 832894

GROUND INFORMATION
Away Supporters' Entrances: No Segregation
Away Supporters' Sections: No Segregation

ADMISSION INFO (1996/97 PRICES)
Adult Standing: £3.00
Adult Seating: £3.00
Child Standing: £1.50
Child Seating: £1.50
Programme Price: 50p (Special games only)
FAX Number: None

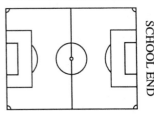

COVERED ENCLOSURE

SCHOOL END

MAIN STAND

Travelling Supporters Information:
Routes: Take A98 towards Cullen and turn left at Drybridge crossroads (for Buckie Town Centre). After 0.5 mile. turn left into West Cathcart Street, then left into Mid Mar Street after 400 yards. Ground adjacent.

CLACHNACUDDIN FC

Founded: 1886
Former Name(s): None
Nickname: 'Lilywhites'
Ground: Grant Street Park, Wyvis Place, Inverness IV3 6BR
Record Attendance: 9,000 vs Rangers (27/8/51)
Colours: Shirts - White
Shorts - Black

Telephone No.: (01463) 238825
Ticket Information: (01463) 710707
Pitch Size: 108 × 70yds
Ground Capacity: 3,000
Seating Capacity: 154
Contact Address: P. Corbett, c/o Club
Contact Phone No.: (01463) 710707

GENERAL INFORMATION
Supporters Club Administrator: None
Address: -
Telephone Number: -
Car Parking: Adjacent to Ground
Coach Parking: Adjacent to Ground
Nearest Railway Station: Inverness
Nearest Bus Station: Inverness
Club Shop: At Ground
Opening Times: Matchdays Only
Telephone No.: (01463) 710707
Postal Sales: Yes
Nearest Police Station: Inverness
Police Force: Northern Constabulary
Police Telephone No.: (01463) 239191

GROUND INFORMATION
Away Supporters' Entrances: No Segregation
Away Supporters' Sections: No Segregation
ADMISSION INFO (1996/97 PRICES)
Adult Standing: £3.00
Child Standing: £1.50
Programme Price: 20p
FAX Number: (01463) 718261

SOCIAL CLUB

COVERED STAND

Travelling Supporters Information:
Routes: From East & South: From roundabout at the junction of A9 and A96 proceed into Town Centre and over River Ness. Turning right at lights (A862 to Dingwall) up Kenneth Street, over roundabout onto Telford Street for 200 yards turning right into Telford Road opposite Fish Shop. At the top turn left on Lower Kessack Street and left again. Left into Wyvis Place, ground is on the left.

COVE RANGERS FC

Founded: 1922
Former Name(s): None
Nickname: None
Ground: Allan Park, Loirston Road, Cove, Aberdeen   AB1 4NS
Record Attendance: 2,300 vs Manchester United (15/11/92) & vs Dunfermline (28/1/95)
Colours: Shirts - Blue
       Shorts - Blue

Telephone No.: (01224) 871467 (Social Club)
Ticket Information: (01224) 871467
Pitch Size: 104 × 65yds
Ground Capacity: 2,300
Seating Capacity: 200
Contact Address: Duncan Little, c/o Club
Contact Phone No.: (01224) 890433 (Work)
Social Club: (01224) 871467

GENERAL INFORMATION

Supporters Club Administrator: Malcolm Runcie
Address: c/o Social Club, Allan Park, Cove, Aberdeen
Telephone Number: (01224) 871467
Car Parking: School Car Park/Loirston Road
Coach Parking: By Police Direction
Nearest Railway Station: Guild St, Aberdeen
Nearest Bus Station: Guild Street, Aberdeen
Club Shop: At Social Club
Opening Times: Matchdays Only
Telephone No.: (01224) 871467
Postal Sales: To John Macleod, c/o Club
Nearest Police Station: Nigg Sub Station
Police Force: Grampian Constabulary
Police Telephone No.: (01224) 639111

GROUND INFORMATION

Away Supporters' Entrances: Loirston Road
Away Supporters' Sections: Loirston Road

ADMISSION INFO (1996/97 PRICES)

Adult Standing: £3.00
Adult Seating: £3.00
Child Standing: £1.50
Child Seating: £1.50
Programme Price: £1.00 (Cup ties only)
FAX Number: (01224) 879023

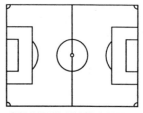

MAIN STAND

OPEN TERRACING

COVERED ENCLOSURE

Travelling Supporters Information:
Routes: From North: Follow signs to Altens/Cove and take the Cove turn-off at the Skean Dhu Hotel roundabout along Loirston Road - Ground 0.5 mile on right; From South: Take the Aberdeen Harbour turn-off some 10 miles north of Stonehaven and continue to Skean Dhu Hotel roundabout - then as North.
Bus Routes: No. 13 bus runs from City Centre to Ground.

DEVERONVALE FC

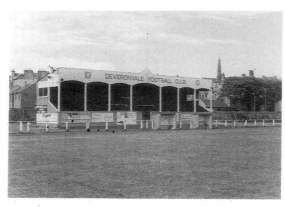

Founded: 1938
Former Name(s): None
Nickname: 'The Vale'
Ground: Princess Royal Park, Bridge Street, Banff
Record Attendance: 5,000 vs Rangers (27/4/52)
Colours: Shirts - Red with White Trim
Shorts - White with Red Trim

Telephone No.: (01261) 818489
Ticket Information: (01261) 818489
Pitch Size: 109 × 78yds
Ground Capacity: 5,000
Seating Capacity: 200
Contact Address: Stewart McPherson, 19 Reid Street, Banff   AB45 1HB
Contact Phone No.: (01261) 818489

GENERAL INFORMATION

Supporters Club Administrator: The Secretary
Address: c/o Club
Telephone Number: (01261) 818489
Car Parking: Street Parking
Coach Parking: Bridge Road Car Park
Nearest Railway Station: Keith (20 miles)
Nearest Bus Station: Macduff (1 mile)
Club Shop: Yes
Opening Times: Matchdays Only
Telephone No.: (01261) 818489
Postal Sales: Yes
Nearest Police Station: Banff
Police Force: Grampian
Police Telephone No.: (01261) 812555

GROUND INFORMATION

Away Supporters' Entrances: No Segregation
Away Supporters' Sections: No Segregation

ADMISSION INFO (1996/97 PRICES)

Adult Standing: £3.00
Adult Seating: £3.50
Child Standing: £1.50
Child Seating: £1.70
Programme Price: 50p
FAX Number: None

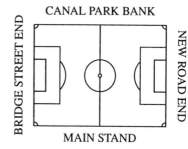

Travelling Supporters Information:
Routes: From Aberdeen: Take first exit on right after Banff Bridge - ground 0.5 mile on left; From Inverness: Travel through Banff on main by-pass and take left turn before Banff Bridge- ground 0.5 mile on left.

ELGIN CITY FC

Founded: 1893
Former Name(s): None
Nickname: 'Black & Whites'
Ground: Borough Briggs, Borough Briggs Road, Elgin
Record Attendance: 11,640 vs Arbroath (17/2/68)
Colours: Shirts - Black & White
　　　　　Shorts - Black & Red

Telephone No.: (01343) 547921
Ticket Information: (01343) 551114
Pitch Size: 120 × 86yds
Ground Capacity: 8,000
Seating Capacity: 450
Contact Address: Peter Strachan, c/o Elgin City FC, 51 Lesmurdie Road, Elgin IV30 2HP
Contact Phone No.: (01343) 542710
Contact FAX No.: (01343) 547921

GENERAL INFORMATION
Supporters Club Administrator: Mrs. C. Jack
Address: c/o Club
Telephone Number: (01343) 542710
Car Parking: At Ground
Coach Parking: At Ground
Nearest Railway Station: Elgin (1 mile)
Nearest Bus Station: Elgin (0.25 mile)
Club Shop: Yes
Opening Times: 8.30am - 5.30pm Weekdays
Telephone No.: (01343) 551114
Postal Sales: Yes
Nearest Police Station: Elgin (1 mile)
Police Force: Grampian
Police Telephone No.: (01343) 543101

GROUND INFORMATION
Away Supporters' Entrances: West End
Away Supporters' Sections: Covered Enclosure

ADMISSION INFO (1996/97 PRICES)
Adult Standing: £3.00
Adult Seating: £4.00
Child Standing: £1.50
Child Seating: £2.00
Programme Price: 50p
FAX Number: (01343) 814133

(SOCIAL CLUB)
MAIN STAND

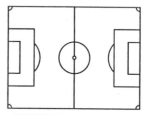

COVERED ENCLOSURE

Travelling Supporters Information:
Routes: Take Alexandra bypass to roundabout 0.5 mile from City Centre and turn left towards Lossiemouth. Borough Briggs Road is on left.

FORRES MECHANICS FC

Founded: 1884
Former Name(s): None
Nickname: 'Can Cans'
Ground: Mosset Park, Lea Road, Forres
Record Attendance: 7,000 vs Celtic (2/2/57)
Colours: Shirts - Chocolate & Gold
Shorts - Gold
Telephone No.: (01309) 675096
Ticket Information: (01309) 675096

Pitch Size: 106 × 69yds
Ground Capacity: 6,540
Seating Capacity: 540
Contact Address: C. C. Fraser, 19 Pilmuir Road West, Forres   IV36 0AN
Contact Phone N°: (01309) 672016 or 672349
OR Contact: Moray G. Cattanach, 8 St.Margarets Court, Forres
Telephone No.: (01309) 676993

GENERAL INFORMATION
Supporters Club Administrator:
Paul Grant
Address: Radnor Place, North Road, Forres
Telephone Number: (01309) 676940
Car Parking: At Ground
Coach Parking: At Ground
Nearest Railway Station: Forres
Nearest Bus Station: Forres
Club Shop: None
Opening Times: -
Telephone No.: -
Postal Sales: -
Nearest Police Station: Forres
Police Force: Grampian
Police Telephone No.: (01309) 672224

GROUND INFORMATION
Away Supporters' Entrances: No Segregation
Away Supporters' Sections: No Segregation

ADMISSION INFO (1996/97 PRICES)
Adult Standing: £3.00
Adult Seating: £4.00
Child Standing: £1.50
Child Seating: £2.50
Programme Price: None
FAX Number: (01309) 675096

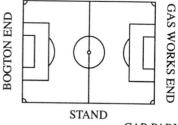

STAND

CAR PARK

Travelling Supporters Information:
Routes: Exit Forres bypass (A940) - Grantown on Spey/Forres Town Centre. Take first left along burn, cross bridge and first left. Stand clearly visible from bypass.

FORT WILLIAM FC

Founded: 1984
Former Name(s): None
Nickname: 'The Fort'
Ground: Claggan Park, Fort William, Inverness-shire
Record Attendance: 1,500 vs Stirling Albion (4/1/86)
Colours: Shirts - Gold & Black
Shorts - Black

Telephone No.: None at Ground
Ticket Information: (01397) 772518
Pitch Size: 102 × 80yds
Ground Capacity: 4,600
Seating Capacity: 400
Contact Address: J. Baird, 11 Clerk Drive, Corpach, Fort William PH33 6LZ
Contact Phone No.: (01397) 772518
Social Club: (01397) 703829

GENERAL INFORMATION
Supporters Club Administrator: None
Address: -
Telephone Number: -
Car Parking: At Ground
Coach Parking: At Ground
Nearest Railway Station: Fort William
Nearest Bus Station: Fort William
Club Shop: None
Opening Times: -
Telephone No.: -
Postal Sales: -
Nearest Police Station: High Street, Fort William
Police Force: Northern Constabulary
Police Telephone No.: (01397) 702361

GROUND INFORMATION
Away Supporters' Entrances: No Segregation
Away Supporters' Sections: No Segregation

ADMISSION INFO (1996/97 PRICES)
Adult Standing: £3.00
Adult Seating: £3.00
Child Standing: £1.50
Child Seating: £1.50
Programme Price: None
FAX Number: (01397) 705627

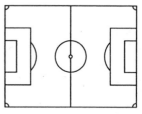

STAND

Travelling Supporters Information:
Routes: From South: Approaching on A82 proceed on by-pass of Town Centre. After 2 roundabouts continue on Belford Road past Railway Station on left and Swimming Baths on right. After 0.5 mile and crossing over the River Nevis, take first right into Claggan Road and ground is 0.5 mile on left.

FRASERBURGH FC

Founded: Circa 1897
Former Name(s): None
Nickname: 'The Broch'
Ground: Bellslea Park, Seaforth Street, Fraserburgh   AB43 5BD
Record Attendance: 5,800 vs Hearts (13/2/54)
Colours: Shirts - Black & White Stripes
           Shorts - Black

Telephone No.: (01346) 518444
Ticket Information: (01346) 541368
Pitch Size: 106 × 66yds
Ground Capacity: 6,000
Seating Capacity: 250
Contact Address: Ian Smith, Bridgend Cottage, Tyrie, Fraserburgh   AB43 4DN
Contact Phone No.: (01346) 541368

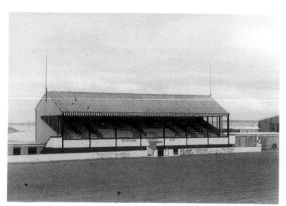

GENERAL INFORMATION
Supporters Club Administrator: Mr. Tasker
Address: c/o The Crown Bar, Shore Street, Fraserburgh
Telephone Number: (01346) 517942
Car Parking: At Ground
Coach Parking: At Ground
Nearest Railway Station: Aberdeen (40 mls)
Nearest Bus Station: Fraserburgh
Club Shop: None
Opening Times: -
Telephone No.: (01346) 519425
Postal Sales: -
Nearest Police Station: Fraserburgh
Police Force: Grampian
Police Telephone No.: (01346) 513121

GROUND INFORMATION
Away Supporters' Entrances: No Segregation
Away Supporters' Sections: No Segregation

ADMISSION INFO (1996/97 PRICES)
Adult Standing: £3.00
Adult Seating: £3.00
Child Standing: £1.50
Child Seating: £1.50
Programme Price: 50p
FAX Number: None

STAND

Travelling Supporters Information:
Routes: Ground is in Town Centre off Seaforth Street (between Town Centre and Harbour).

HUNTLY FC

Founded: 1928
Former Name(s): None
Nickname: None
Ground: Christie Park, East Park Street, Huntly, Aberdeenshire
Record Attendance: 4,500 v Dundee United (18/2/95)
Colours: Shirts - Black & Gold
Shorts - Black

Telephone No.: (01466) 793548
Ticket Information: (01466) 793548
Pitch Size: 105 × 72yds
Ground Capacity: 4,500
Seating Capacity: 270
Contact Address: Peter Morrison, Glenlea, Littlejohn Street, Huntly   AB54 5HL
Contact Phone No.: (01466) 793269

GENERAL INFORMATION
Supporters Club Administrator: None
Address: -
Telephone Number: -
Car Parking: At Ground
Coach Parking: At Ground
Nearest Railway Station: Huntly (1 mile)
Nearest Bus Station: Huntly (0.25 mile)
Club Shop: Yes
Opening Times: Matchdays Only
Telephone No.: -
Postal Sales: -
Nearest Police Station: Adjacent to Ground
Police Force: Grampian
Police Telephone No.: (01466) 792246

GROUND INFORMATION
Away Supporters' Entrances: No Segregation
Away Supporters' Sections: No Segregation

ADMISSION INFO (1996/97 PRICES)
Adult Standing: £3.00
Adult Seating: £3.00
Child Standing: £1.50
Child Seating: £3.00
Programme Price: 50p
FAX Number: None

```
                    STAND
          ┌─────────────────────────┐
  E       │  ┌──┐          ┌──┐      │
  A       │  │  │    ○     │  │      │
  S       │  │  │   ( )    │  │      │
  T       │  └──┘          └──┘      │
          │                         │
  P       └─────────────────────────┘
  A        COVERED ENCLOSURE
  R
  K
  S
  T
  R
  E
  E
  T
```

Travelling Supporters Information:
Routes: Enter Town off A96 and proceed along King George V Avenue & Gordon Street, pass through Town Centre Square, along Castle Street to East Park Street. Ground is on right before castle.

KEITH FC

Founded: 1919	**Telephone No.**: (01542) 887407
Former Name(s): None	**Pitch Size**: 110 × 75yds
Nickname: 'Maroons'	**Ground Capacity**: 5,500
Ground: Kynoch Park, Balloch Road, Keith	**Seating Capacity**: 450
Record Attendance: 5,820 vs Celtic (4/2/28)	**Contact Address**: Norman Brown, Maravale,
Colours: Shirts - Maroon with Sky Blue Trim	51 Land Street, Keith AB55 3AN
Shorts - Sky Blue	**Contact Phone No.**: (01542) 887407/886182

GENERAL INFORMATION

Supporters Club Administrator: None
Address: -
Telephone Number: -
Car Parking: Balloch Road/Moss Street/ Reidhaven Square
Coach Parking: Balloch Road or Bridge Street Coach Park
Nearest Railway Station: Keith (1 mile)
Nearest Bus Station: Keith
Club Shop: Keith FC Promotions, 29 Regent Street, Keith
Opening Times: Monday-Friday 8.30-4.30
Telephone No.: (01542) 882629
Postal Sales: Yes
Nearest Police Station: Turner Street
Police Force: Grampian
Police Telephone No.: (01542) 882502

GROUND INFORMATION

Away Supporters' Entrances: No Segregation
Away Supporters' Sections: except for cup ties

ADMISSION INFO (1996/97 PRICES)

Adult Standing: £3.00
Adult Seating: £4.00
Child Standing: £1.50
Child Seating: £2.00
Programme Price: 50p
FAX Number: None

MAIN STAND

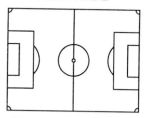

COVERED ENCLOSURE

Travelling Supporters Information:
Routes: From Aberdeen: Coming in on A96, turn right, up Bridge Street (across from Bus Stop at Reidhaven Square), then first left onto Balloch Road; From Inverness: Coming in on A96, turn second left after Citroen Keith Garage in Moss Street onto Balloch Road.

LOSSIEMOUTH FC

Founded: 1945
Former Name(s): None
Nickname: 'Coasters'
Ground: Grant Park, Kellas Avenue,
Lossiemouth   IV31 6JG
Record Attendance: Over 6,000 (During 50's)
Colours: Shirts - Red
       Shorts - Red
Telephone No.: (01343) 813717 - Park

(01343) 813168 - Social Club
Ticket Information: (01343) 813328
Pitch Size: 110 × 60yds
Ground Capacity: 3,500
Seating Capacity: 250
Contact Address: Alan McIntosh, 3 Forties
Place, Lossiemouth   IV31 6SS
Contact Phone No.: (01343) 813328

GENERAL INFORMATION
Supporters Club Administrator:
W. MacDonald
Address: 5 Woodland Walk, Lossiemouth
Telephone Number: (01343) 813739
Car Parking: At Ground
Coach Parking: At Ground
Nearest Railway Station: Elgin
Nearest Bus Station: Lossiemouth
Club Shop: Yes
Opening Times: Matchdays only
Telephone No.: (01343) 813739
Postal Sales: Yes
Nearest Police Station: Lossiemouth
Police Force: Grampian
Police Telephone No.: (01343) 812022

GROUND INFORMATION
Away Supporters' Entrances: No Segregation
Away Supporters' Sections: No Segregation
ADMISSION INFO (1996/97 PRICES)
Adult Seating & Standing: £3.00
Child Seating & Standing: £1.50
Programme Price: None
FAX Number: -

STAND

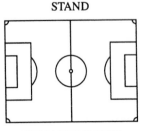

SOCIAL CLUB

NEW ENCLOSURE

Travelling Supporters Information:
Routes: Take Main Road into Lossiemouth and turn 2nd right. Turn right again after 100 yards.

NAIRN COUNTY FC

Founded: 1914	**Telephone No.**: (01667) 454298
Former Name(s): None	**Pitch Size**: 110 × 62yds
Nickname: 'The Wee County'	**Ground Capacity**: 3,800
Ground: Station Park, Balblair Road, Nairn	**Seating Capacity**: 250
Record Attendance: 4,000 (Highland Cup Final 1950)	**Contact Address**: John McNeill, 50 Station Road, Ardersier, Inverness IV1 2ST
Colours: Shirts - Yellow & Black Shorts - Black	**Contact Phone No.**: (01667) 462510

GENERAL INFORMATION

Supporters Club Administrator: None
Address: -
Telephone Number: -
Car Parking: At Ground
Coach Parking: At Ground
Nearest Railway Station: Nairn (Adjacent)
Nearest Bus Station: King St., Nairn (0.5ml)
Club Shop: At Social Club
Opening Times: Club Hours Only
Telephone No.: (01667) 453286
Postal Sales: c/o Steven Bain, 8 Mill Road Terrace, Nairn
Nearest Police Station: King Street, Nairn
Police Force: Northern Constabulary
Police Telephone No.: (01667) 452222

GROUND INFORMATION

Away Supporters' Entrances: No Segregation
Away Supporters' Sections: No Segregation

ADMISSION INFO (1996/97 PRICES)

Adult Standing: £3.00
Adult Seating: £3.00
Child Standing: £1.50
Child Seating: £1.50
Programme Price: 50p
FAX Number: None

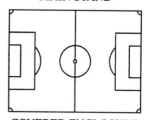

Travelling Supporters Information:
Routes: Ground is situated on the south side of Nairn at the bottom of the Main Street, adjacent to the Railway Station.

PETERHEAD FC

Founded: 1891	**Telephone No.**: (01779) 478256
Former Name(s): None	**Pitch Size**: 110 × 74yds
Nickname: 'Blue Toon'	**Ground Capacity**: 2,500
Ground: Recreation Park, Hay Crescent,	**Seating Capacity**: 300
Peterhead AB42 6HD	**Contact Address**: William G. Campbell, 45
Record Attendance: 8,525 vs Raith (25/2/87)	St. Peter Street, Peterhead AB42 6QD
Colours: Shirts - Royal Blue / White Sleeves	**Contact Phone No.**: (01779) 472954
Shorts - White	

GENERAL INFORMATION
Supporters Club Administrator: None
Address: -
Telephone Number: -
Car Parking: At Ground
Coach Parking: At Ground
Nearest Railway Station: Aberdeen
Nearest Bus Station: Peterhead
Club Shop: None
Opening Times: -
Telephone No.: -
Postal Sales: -
Nearest Police Station: Peterhead
Police Force: Grampian
Police Telephone No.: (01779) 472571

GROUND INFORMATION
Away Supporters' Entrances: No Segregation
Away Supporters' Sections: No Segregation

ADMISSION INFO (1996/97 PRICES)
Adult Standing: £3.00
Adult Seating: £3.50
Child Standing: £1.50
Child Seating: £2.00
Programme Price: 50p
FAX Number: (01779) 475075

(CAR PARK)
COVERED   SOCIAL
ENCLOSURE   CLUB

(QUEEN STREET)

GRANDSTAND
(HAY CRESCENT)

Travelling Supporters Information:
Routes: Ground is situated on left of main road from Fraserburgh (A952). The A952 becomes Queen Street and the ground is opposite the swimming pool.

EAST OF SCOTLAND FOOTBALL LEAGUE

Founded
1930

Secretary
Mr. J. Greenhorn

Address
2 Baberton Mains Court,
Edinburgh

Phone
(0131) 538-0289

ANNAN ATHLETIC FC

1996/97 Season: Premier Division

Ground Address: Galabank, North Street, Annan, Dumfries & Galloway

Telephone N°: (01461) 204108

Year Founded: 1942

Nickname: None

Former Names: Solway Star

Ground Capacity: 2,000

Seating Capacity: None

Club Colours:
Black & Gold Vertical Striped shirts. Black shorts

Contact Address:
A. Irving,
Secretary,
1 Newlands Rise,
Annan,
DG12 5HT

Contact Phone N°:
(01461) 203702

CRAIGROYSTON FC

1996/97 Season: Premier Division

Ground Address: City Park, Ferry Road, Edinburgh

Telephone N°: None

Year Founded: 1976

Nickname: 'Craigie'

Former Names: None

Ground Capacity: n/a

Seating Capacity: n/a

Club Colours:
Yellow Shirts.
Blue Shorts

Contact Address:
Willie Pryde,
Secretary,
17 Brunswick Terrace,
Edinburgh
EH7 5PG

Contact Phone N°:
(0131) 557-5389

EDINBURGH CITY FC

1996/97 Season: Premier Division
Ground Address: Meadowbank Stadium, London Road, Edinburgh, EH7 6AE
Telephone Nº: (0131) 661-5351

Year Founded: 1928 (re-formed 1986)
Nickname: 'The City'
Former Names: None
Ground Capacity: n/a
Seating Capacity: None

Club Colours:
White Shirts
Black Shorts

Contact Address:
A. Brown,
Secretary,
1 Sighthill Street,
Edinburgh,
EH11 4QQ

Contact Phone Nº:
(0131) 453-5827

EDINBURGH UNIVERSITY AFC

1996/97 Season: Premier Division

Ground Address: Peffermill Playing Fields, Peffermill Road, Edinburgh
Telephone Nº: (0131) 667-7541

Year Founded: 1878
Nickname: 'The Burgh'
Former Names: None
Ground Capacity: 212
Seating Capacity: 12

Club Colours:
Green Shirts.
Blue Shorts.

Contact Address:
T. Haines,
Edinburgh Univ. Sports Union,
48 Pleasance,
Edinburgh,
EH8 9TJ

Contact Phone Nº:
(0131) 650-2346

GALA FAIRYDEAN FC

1996/97 Season: Premier Division	**Year Founded**: 1907
	Nickname: 'The Dean'
Ground Address: Netherdale,	**Former Names**: None
Galashiels	**Ground Capacity**: 5,500
Telephone Nº: (01896) 753554	**Seating Capacity**: 495

Club Colours:
Black & White Shirts.
Black & White Shorts.

Contact Address:
George McGill,
Secretary,
25 Melrose Road,
Galashiels

Contact Phone Nº:
(01896) 754500
FAX: (01896) 757749

MANOR THISTLE FC

1996/97 Season: Premier Division	**Year Founded**: 1968
	Nickname: 'The Crew'
Ground Address: Muirhouse Sports	**Former Names**: None
Ground, Marine Drive, Edinburgh	**Ground Capacity**: 500 Approx.
Telephone Nº: (0131) 332-0650	**Seating Capacity**: None

Club Colours:
Maroon shirts with Sky Blue
trim. White shorts, maroon socks

Contact Address:
Mr. I. Gracie,
Secretary,
27 Morton Street,
Edinburgh,

Contact Phone Nº:
(0131) 556-7843

PENCAITLAND FC

1996/97 Season: Premier Division

Ground Address: Pencaitland Park, Pencaitland, East Lothian
Telephone N°: None

Year Founded: 1884
Nickname: None
Former Names: Pencaitland Amateur
Ground Capacity: 1,000
Seating Capacity: None

Club Colours:
Maroon & White Shirts.
White Shorts.

Contact Address:
J.M. Greenhorn,
2 Baberton Main Court,
Edinburgh

Contact Phone N°:
(0131) 538-0289

PRESTON ATHLETIC FC

1996/97 Season: Premier Division

Ground Address: Pennypit Park, Rope Walk, Prestonpans, E. Lothian
Telephone N°: None

Year Founded: 1945
Nickname: 'Panners'
Former Names: None
Ground Capacity: 4,000
Seating Capacity: 313

Club Colours:
Navy Blue with Red & White
Trim Shirts.
Navy Blue Shorts.

Contact Address:
J. Adams,
1 Magdalene Place,
Edinburgh
EH15 6BJ

Contact Phone N°:
(0131) 669-8293

THE SPARTANS FC

1996/97 Season: Premier Division

Ground Address: City Park, Ferry Road, Edinburgh
Telephone Nº: None

Year Founded: 1951
Nickname: None
Former Names: None
Ground Capacity: 3,000
Seating Capacity: None

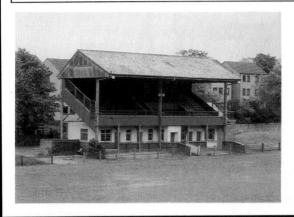

Club Colours:
White Shirts.
Red Shorts.

Contact Address:
D. Gilbraith,
Secretary,
12 Gardiners Crescent,
Edinburgh,
EH14 1EY

Contact Phone Nº:
(0131) 229-9845

WHITEHILL WELFARE FC

1996/97 Season: Premier Division

Ground Address: Ferguson Park, Carnethie Street, Rosewell, Midlothian
Telephone Nº: (0131) 440-0115

Year Founded: 1953
Nickname: 'The Welfare'
Former Names: None
Ground Capacity: 4,000
Seating Capacity: None

Club Colours:
Shirts are Maroon with Sky Blue Sleeves. White shorts.

Contact Address:
Peter McGauley,
47 Prestonhall Crescent,
Rosewell,
Midlothian

Contact Phone Nº:
(0131) 440-3417

CIVIL SERVICE STROLLERS FC

1996/97 Season: First Division

Ground Address: Muirhouse Sports Ground, Marine Drive, Edinburgh
Telephone Nº: (0131) 332-0650

Year Founded: 1908
Nickname: 'Strollers'
Former Names: None
Ground Capacity: 500 Approx.
Seating Capacity: None

Club Colours:
Shirts are White with Thin Dark Blue Candy Stripe. Blue shorts.

Contact Address:
T. Stevenson,
Secretary,
292 Gilmerton Road,
Edinburgh

Contact Phone Nº:
(0131) 664-2368

COLDSTREAM FC

1996/97 Season: First Division

Ground Address: Home Park, Coldstream, Berwickshire
Telephone Nº: (01890) 883085

Year Founded: 1895
Nickname: 'The Streamers'
Former Names: None
Ground Capacity: -
Seating Capacity: -

Club Colours:
Royal Blue Shirts.
Blue Shorts

Contact Address:
Mr. T.G. Tait,
Secretary,
25 Duns Road,
Coldstream

Contact Phone Nº:
(01890) 882685

EASTHOUSES LILY (M.W.) FC

1996/97 Season: First Division

Ground Address: Newbattle Complex, Easthouses

Telephone N°: None

Year Founded: 1969
Nickname: 'Houses'
Former Names: None
Ground Capacity: 1,500
Seating Capacity: None

NO PHOTOGRAPH

AVAILABLE AT THE

TIME OF PUBLICATION

Club Colours:
Red Shirts
White Shorts

Contact Address:
R. Paul,
Secretary,
90 Langlaw Road,
Mayfield,
Dalkeith

Contact Phone N°:
(0131) 663-9768

EYEMOUTH UNITED FC

1996/97 Season: First Division

Ground Address: Gunsgreen Park, Johns Road, Eyemouth, Berwickshire

Telephone N°: None

Year Founded: 1948
Nickname: 'The Fishermen'
Former Names: None
Ground Capacity: n/a
Seating Capacity: n/a

Club Colours:
Maroon Shirts.
White Shorts.

Contact Address:
John Windram,
Secretary,
Eyemouth United FC
'Kintyre', Upper Houndlaw,
Eyemouth
Berwickshire

Contact Phone N°:
(018907) 50601

HAWICK ROYAL ALBERT FC

1996/97 Season: First Division

Ground Address: Albert Park, Mansfield Road, Hawick
Telephone Nº: (01450) 374231

Year Founded: 1947
Nickname: 'The Albert'
Former Names: None
Ground Capacity: 2,000
Seating Capacity: 500

Club Colours:
Royal Blue Shirts.
White Shorts.

Contact Address:
D. Telfer,
Secretary,
20 Orchard Terrace,
Hawick

Contact Phone Nº:
(01450) 372893

HERIOT-WATT UNIVERSITY FC

1996/97 Season: First Division

Ground Address: H.W. Univ. Riccarton Campus, Riccarton, Edinburgh
Telephone Nº: (0131) 449-5111

Year Founded: 1942
Nickname: 'The Watt'
Former Names: None
Ground Capacity: n/a
Seating Capacity: n/a

Club Colours:
Blue & Yellow Shirts.
Blue Shorts.

Contact Address:
M. Burns,
16 Dudley Crescent,
Edinburgh

Contact Phone Nº:
(0131) 554-2453

KELSO UNITED FC

1996/97 Season: First Division	Year Founded: 1924
	Nickname: 'Tweedsiders'
Ground Address: Woodside Park,	Former Names: None
Kelso, Roxburghshire	Ground Capacity: 1,000
Telephone Nº: (01573) 223780	Seating Capacity: None

Club Colours:
Black & White Vertical Striped shirts. Black shorts.

Contact Address:
A. H. Douglas,
Secretary,
34 Dyers Court,
Kelso,
TD5 7NQ

Contact Phone Nº:
(01573) 225314

LOTHIAN THISTLE FC

1996/97 Season: First Division	Year Founded: 1969
	Nickname: 'Thistle'
Ground Address: Campbell Park,	Former Names: None
Woodhall Road, Colinton, Edinburgh	Ground Capacity: 1,000
Telephone Nº: None	Seating Capacity: None

Club Colours:
Blue shirts.
White shorts.

Contact Address:
Tom Allison,
Secretary,
31 Clermiston Place,
Edinburgh,
EH4 7DN

Contact Phone Nº:
(0131) 336-1751

PEEBLES ROVERS FC

1996/97 Season: First Division

Ground Address: Whitestone Park, Peebles
Telephone Nº: None

Year Founded: 1894
Nickname: 'The Rovers'
Former Names: None
Ground Capacity: 3,000
Seating Capacity: 500

Club Colours:
Red & White Shirts.
Red & White Shorts.

Contact Address:
C. Morrish,
8 Springhill Road,
Peebles,
EH45 9EW

Contact Phone Nº:
(01721) 720543

SELKIRK FC

1996/97 Season: First Division

Ground Address: Ettrick Park, Riverside Road, Selkirk, Selkirkshire
Telephone Nº: None

Year Founded: 1880
Nickname: 'Souters'
Former Names: None
Ground Capacity: 3,000
Seating Capacity: None

Club Colours:
Shirts and Shorts are Royal Blue with White Trim.

Contact Address:
A. Skeldon,
47A Curor Street,
Selkirk

Contact Phone Nº:
(01750) 23020

TOLLCROSS UNITED FC

1996/97 Season: First Division
Ground Address: Fernieside
Recreation park, Fernieside Avenue,
Edinburgh
Telephone Nº: None

Year Founded: 1971
Nickname: 'The Cross'
Former Names: None
Ground Capacity: 400
Seating Capacity: None

Club Colours:
Red Shirts with White Sleeves.
White Shorts.

Contact Address:
Alistair Wilkie,
36 Broomhall Place,
Edinburgh

Contact Phone Nº:
(0131) 539-0225

VALE OF LEITHEN FC

1996/97 Season: First Division

Ground Address: Victoria Park,
Innerleithen
Telephone Nº: None

Year Founded: 1891
Nickname: 'Vale'
Former Names: None
Ground Capacity: 3,500
Seating Capacity: None

Club Colours:
Navy Blue Shirts.
White Shorts.

Contact Address:
I. Haggarty,
11 Peebles Road,
Innerleithen
EH44 6QX

Contact Phone Nº:
(01896) 830995

THE SOUTH OF SCOTLAND FOOTBALL LEAGUE

Secretary
R. Shaw

Address
8 Kirkland Road, Heathall
Dumfries,   DG1 3RN

Phone
(01387) 61736

ANNAN ATHLETIC 'A' FC

Ground Address: Galabank, North Street, Annan, Dumfries & Galloway
Telephone Nº: (01461) 204108

Year Founded: 1942
Nickname: None
Former Names: Solway Star
Ground Capacity: 2,000
Seating Capacity: None

Club Colours:
Black & Gold Vertical Striped shirts. Black shorts

Contact Address:
A. Irving,
Secretary,
1 Newlands Rise,
Annan,
DG12 5HT

Contact Phone Nº:
(01461) 203702

BLACKWOOD DYNAMOS FC

Ground Address: Crichton Hospital Park, Dumfries, Dumfries & Galloway
Telephone Nº: None

Year Founded: 1972
Nickname: 'Dynamos'
Former Names: None
Ground Capacity: 2,500
Seating Capacity: None

Club Colours:
Blue & White Striped shirts. Black shorts

Contact Address:
Kenneth Cameron,
26 Lochaber Walk,
Dumfries,
DG2 9QE

Contact Phone Nº:
(01387) 265930

CREETOWN FC

Ground Address: Castle Cary Football Ground, Creetown, Dumfries & Galloway
Telephone Nº: None

Year Founded: 1895
Nickname: 'Ferrytown'
Former Names: None
Ground Capacity: 2,000
Seating Capacity: None

Club Colours:
Black & Gold Shirts.
Black Shorts

Contact Address:
Robert Ross,
Secretary,
9 Silver Street,
Creetown,
DG8 7HU

Contact Phone Nº:
(0161) 820531

DALBEATTIE STAR FC

Ground Address: Islecroft Stadium, Dalbeattie, Dumfries & Galloway
Telephone Nº: None

Year Founded: 1902
Nickname: 'The Star'
Former Names: None Known
Ground Capacity: 3,500
Seating Capacity: 300

Club Colours:
Red & Black Striped Shirts
Black Shorts

Contact Address:
Frank Styles,
Secretary,
4 Queens Grove,
Dalbeattie,
DG5 4JG

Contact Phone Nº:
(01556) 611154

DUMFRIES HIGH SCHOOL FORMER PUPILS

Ground Address: Barbour Hall, Glencaple, Dumfries
Telephone Nº: –

Year Founded: 1970
Nickname: 'Dumfries F.P's'
Former Names: None
Ground Capacity: 2,000
Seating Capacity: None

Club Colours:
Yellow Shirts.
Green Shorts.

Contact Address:
A. Gass,
Secretary,
23 Oakfield Drive,
Dumfries,
DG1 4PD

Contact Phone Nº:
(01387) 268838

GIRVAN FC

Ground Address: Hamilton Park, Vicarton Street, Girvan, Ayrshire KA26
Telephone Nº: None

Year Founded: 1947
Nickname: 'The Amateurs'
Former Names: Girvan Amateurs
Ground Capacity: 5,000
Seating Capacity: 200

Club Colours:
Shirts - Royal Blue with White Collar. Royal Blue Shorts.

Contact Address:
J.M. Irvine,
Secretary,
8 Snow Street,
Girvan,
KA26 0DZ

Contact Phone Nº:
(01465) 712702

MAXWELLTOWN H.S.O.B. FC

Ground Address: Maxwelltown High School, Lochside Road, Dumfries
Telephone N°: None

Year Founded: Not Known
Nickname: None
Former Names: None
Ground Capacity: -
Seating Capacity: -

Contact Address:
Barry Johnstone,
Netherwood,
Gillbrae Road,
Dumfries,
DG1 4EJ

Contact Phone N°:
(01387) 64300

NEWTON STEWART FC

Ground Address: Blairmount Park, Newton Stewart, Dumfries & Galloway
Telephone N°: None

Year Founded: Not Known
Nickname: None
Former Names: None
Ground Capacity: 1,500
Seating Capacity: 100

Club Colours:
Black & White Striped Shirts
Black Shorts

Contact Address:
T. Irvine,
6 Racegreen Avenue,
Minnigaff,
Newton Stewart,
DG8 6PL

Contact Phone N°:
(01671) 402866

St. Cuthbert's Wanderers FC

Ground Address: St. Marys Park, Castledykes Road, Kirkcudbright, Dumfries & Galloway
Telephone N°: None

Year Founded: 1879
Nickname: 'Saints'
Former Names: None
Ground Capacity: 6,500
Seating Capacity: 210

Club Colours:
Shirts – Blue with White Hoops
Blue Shorts.

Contact Address:
W. J. McKenzie,
34 Castle Street,
Kirkcudbright,
DG6 4JD

Contact Phone N°:
(01557) 330680

Stranraer Athletic FC

Ground Address: Stranraer Academy, London Road, Stranraer, Dumfries & Galloway
Telephone N°: None

Year Founded: 1995
Nickname: None
Former Names: None
Ground Capacity: 1,000
Seating Capacity: None

Club Colours:
Blue Shirts.
White Shorts.

Contact Address:
Mr. Colin Arkless,
17 Lewis Street,
Stranraer,
Dumfries & Galloway

Contact Phone N°:
(01776) 705942

TARFF ROVERS FC

Ground Address: Ballgreen Park, Kirkgowan, Nr. Newton Stewart DG8
Telephone Nº: None

Year Founded: 1874
Nickname: 'The Rovers'
Former Names: None
Ground Capacity: 4,040
Seating Capacity: 40

Club Colours:
Green with Black Trim Shirts. Black Shorts

Contact Address:
N. McColm,
20 Avon Place,
Edinburgh
EH4 6RE

Contact Phone Nº:
(0131) 317-1601

THREAVE ROVERS FC

Ground Address: Meadow Park, Castle Douglas, Dumfries & Galloway
Telephone Nº: (01556) 504536

Year Founded: 1953
Nickname: 'Rovers'
Former Names: None
Ground Capacity: 1,500
Seating Capacity: None

Club Colours:
Black & White Striped Shirts. Black Shorts.

Contact Address:
Ian Bendall,
Newmarket Street,
Castle Douglas,
DG7 3LP

Contact Phone Nº:
(01556) 650310

WIGTOWN & BLADNOCH FC

Ground Address: Trammonford Park, Wigtown, Dumfries & Galloway **Telephone Nº**: (01988) 402323	**Year Founded**: 1880 **Nickname**: None **Former Names**: None **Ground Capacity**: 1,500 **Seating Capacity**: None

Club Colours:
Red & White Striped Shirts.
Red Shorts.

Contact Address:
D. McGinn,
21 Beddie Crescent,
Wigtown,
DG8 9HX

Contact Phone Nº:
(01988) 403308

SOCCER BOOK PUBLISHING LTD.
72 ST. PETER'S AVENUE
CLEETHORPES
N.E. LINCOLNSHIRE
DN35 8HU

Phone (01472) 696226
FAX (01472) 698546

BACK NUMBERS

We still have the undermentioned publications available post free at the reduced prices shown. There are very few remaining copies of some of these titles so, please, order any that you require without delay to avoid disappointment.

Year	TITLE	Price	Qty	Order Value
1990	The Supporters' Guide to Football League Clubs 1991	£2.95		
1991	The Supporters' Guide to Football League Clubs 1992	£3.99		
1992	The Supporters' Guide to Football League Clubs 1993	£3.99		
1992	The Supporters' Guide to Scottish Football 1993	£2.99		
1993	The Supporters' Guide to Premier & Football League Clubs 1994	£3.99		
1993	The Supporters' Guide to Scottish Football 1994	£3.99		
1993	The Supporters' Guide to Welsh Football 1994	£3.99		
1994	The Supporters' Guide to Premier & Football League Clubs 1995	£3.99		
1994	The Supporters' Guide to Scottish Football 1995	£3.99		
1994	The Supporters' Guide to Non-League Football 1995	£3.99		
1994	The Supporters' Guide to Welsh Football 1995	£3.99		
1995	The Supporters' Guide to Premier & Football League Clubs 1996	£3.99		
1995	The Supporters' Guide to Scottish Football 1996	£3.99		
1995	The Supporters' Guide to Non-League Football 1996	£3.99		
1995	The Supporters' Guide to Welsh Football 1996	£3.99		
1995	The Supporters' Guide to Football Programmes 1996	£3.99		

SCOTLAND INTERNATIONAL LINE-UPS AND STATISTICS 1995

29 March 1995
v RUSSIA (ECQ) *Moscow*

Leighton	Hibernian
McKimmie	Aberdeen
Boyd	Celtic
McLaren	Rangers
Hendry	Blackburn Rovers
Calderwood	Tottenham Hotspur
Jackson	Hibernian (sub. Shearer)
McStay	Celtic
McGinlay	Bolton Wanderers (sub. McKinlay)
McAllister	Leeds United
Collins	Celtic

Result 0-0

26 April 1995
v SAN MARINO (ECQ) *Serravalle*

Leighton	Hibernian
Calderwood	Tottenham Hotspur
Boyd	Celtic
McLaren	Rangers
Hendry	Blackburn Rovers
Jackson	Hibernian
Nevin	Tranmere Rovers (sub. McKinlay)
Shearer	Aberdeen
McGinlay	Bolton Wanderers (sub. Spencer)
McAllister	Leeds United
Collins	Celtic

Result 2-0 Collins, Calderwood

21 May 1995
v JAPAN *Hiroshima*

Leighton	Hibernian
McLaren	Rangers
McKinnon	Motherwell
Martin	Motherwell
Calderwood	Tottenham Hotspur (sub. Whyte)
Lambert	Motherwell
McKinlay	Dundee United
Spencer	Chelsea
Gemmill	Nottingham Forest (sub. Bernard)
Jackson	Hibernian
Burley	Chelsea

Result 0-0

24 May 1995
v ECUADOR *Toyama*

Leighton	Hibernian
McLaren	Rangers
Martin	Motherwell
Calderwood	Tottenham Hotspur
Bernard	Oldham Athletic
McKinlay	Dundee United
Gemmill	Nottingham Forest
Jackson	Hibernian (sub. Crawford)
Whyte	Middlesbrough (sub. Lambert)
Robertson	Heart of Midlothian
Burley	Chelsea

Result 2-1 Robertson, Crawford

7 June 1995
v FAROE ISLANDS (ECQ) *Toftir*

Leighton	Hibernian
McKimmie	Aberdeen
McKinnon	Motherwell
McLaren	Rangers
Calderwood	Tottenham Hotspur
Burley	Chelsea
Jackson	Hibernian
McKinlay	Dundee United
McGinlay	Bolton Wanderers (sub. Gemmill)
Collins	Celtic
Shearer	Aberdeen (sub. Robertson)

Result 2-0 McKinlay, McGinlay

16 August 1995
v GREECE (ECQ) *Hampden Park*

Leighton	Hibernian
Calderwood	Tottenham Hotspur
McKimmie	Aberdeen
Boyd	Celtic
Burley	Chelsea
McCall	Rangers
McAllister	Leeds United
Collins	Celtic
McKinlay	Celtic
Jackson	Hibernian (sub. Robertson)
Shearer	Aberdeen (sub. McCoist)

Result 1-0 McCoist

6 September 1995
v FINLAND (ECQ) *Hampden Park*

Leighton	Hibernian
Calderwood	Tottenham Hotspur
Hendry	Blackburn Rovers
Boyd	Celtic
McKimmie	Aberdeen (sub. W. McKinlay)
McLaren	Rangers
McAllister	Leeds United
Collins	Celtic
T. McKinlay	Celtic
Booth	Aberdeen (sub. Jackson)
Spencer	Chelsea (sub. McCoist)

Result 1-0 Booth

11 October 1995
v SWEDEN *Rasunda Stadium, Solna*

Leighton	Hibernian (sub. Goram)
McKimmie	Aberdeen
Calderwood	Tottenham Hotspur
Hendry	Blackburn Rovers
Burley	Chelsea (sub. W. McKinlay)
McAllister	Leeds United (sub. Jackson)
McLaren	Rangers
Collins	Celtic
Boyd	Celtic
Robertson	Heart of Midlothian (sub. Nevin)
McGinlay	Bolton Wanderers (sub. Jess)

Result 0-2

SCOTLAND INTERNATIONAL LINE-UPS AND STATISTICS 1995-96

15 November 1995
SAN MARINO (ECQ) *Hampden Park*
Leighton	Hibernian
McLaren	Rangers
Boyd	Celtic
Calderwood	Tottenham Hotspur
Hendry	Blackburn Rovers
Gemmill	Nottingham Forest
Nevin	Tranmere Rovers
Booth	Aberdeen (sub. Jackson)
Jess	Aberdeen
McAllister	Leeds United (sub. McCoist)
Collins	Celtic (sub. W. McKinlay)

Result 5-0 Jess, Booth, McCoist, Nevin, Francini (og)

27 March 1996
AUSTRALIA *Hampden Park*
Leighton	Hibernian
Burley	Chelsea
Boyd	Celtic
O'Neil	Celtic (sub. Gallacher)
Hendry	Blackburn Rovers
W. McKinlay	Blackburn Rovers (sub. Jackson)
Spencer	Chelsea
McStay	Celtic (sub. Booth)
McCoist	Rangers (sub. Nevin)
McAllister	Leeds United
Collins	Celtic

Result 1-0 McCoist

24 April 1996
DENMARK *Copenhagen*
Leighton	Hibernian (sub. Goram)
McKimmie	Aberdeen
T. McKinlay	Celtic
Boyd	Celtic
Hendry	Blackburn Rovers (sub. W. McKinlay)
McCall	Rangers (sub. Gemmill)
Burley	Chelsea
Gallacher	Blackburn Rovers (sub. McCoist)
Spencer	Chelsea (sub. Jackson)
McAllister	Leeds United
Collins	Celtic

Result 0-2

26 May 1996
U.S.A. *Willowbrook Park, Conneticut*
Leighton	Hibernian (sub. Walker)
Boyd	Celtic
Burley	Chelsea (sub. McCall)
Calderwood	Tottenham Hotspur
Hendry	Blackburn Rovers
Whyte	Middlesbrough
Jess	Coventry City
Jackson	Hibernian (sub. Collins)
Gemmill	Nottingham Forest (sub. McAllister)
Booth	Aberdeen
Durie	Rangers (sub. Spencer)

Result 1-2 Durie

30 May 1996
COLOMBIA *Orange Bowl, Miami*
Goram	Rangers
McKimmie	Aberdeen
T. McKinlay	Celtic
Boyd	Celtic
Hendry	Blackburn Rovers (sub. Burley)
Calderwood	Tottenham Hotspur
Collins	Celtic
McAllister	Leeds United
McCall	Rangers
McCoist	Rangers (sub. Gallacher)
Spencer	Chelsea (sub. Jess)

Result 0-1

10 June 1996
HOLLAND (EC) *Villa Park*
Goram	Rangers
McKimmie	Aberdeen (sub. Burley)
Boyd	Celtic
Calderwood	Tottenham Hotspur
Hendry	Blackburn Rovers
Gallacher	Blackburn Rovers (sub. B. McKinlay)
McCall	Rangers
McAllister	Leeds United
Collins	Celtic
Booth	Aberdeen (sub. Spencer)
Durie	Rangers

Result 0-0

15 June 1996
ENGLAND (EC) *Wembley*
Goram	Rangers
McKimmie	Aberdeen
Boyd	Celtic
Calderwood	Tottenham Hotspur
Hendry	Blackburn Rovers
Spencer	Chelsea (sub. McCoist)
McCall	Rangers
McAllister	Leeds United
Collins	Celtic
T. McKinlay	Celtic (sub. Burley)
Durie	Rangers (sub. Jess)

Result 0-2

18 June 1996
SWITZERLAND (EC) *Villa Park*
Goram	Rangers
McKimmie	Aberdeen
Boyd	Celtic
Calderwood	Tottenham Hotspur
Hendry	Blackburn Rovers
McCall	Rangers
McCoist	Rangers (sub. Spencer)
McAllister	Leeds United
Collins	Celtic
T. McKinlay	Celtic (sub. Booth)
Durie	Rangers (sub. Jess)

Result 1-0 McCoist